AI for Absolute Beginners:
A Clear Guide to Tomorrow

Book 1 in the AI, Data Science, Python & Statistics for Beginners Series

Oliver Theobald

Published by Scatterplot Press

First Edition

www.scatterplotpress.com

ISBN: 978-1-913666-28-6

For feedback, print quality issues, media contact, omissions or errors regarding this book, please contact the author at **oliver.theobald@scatterplotpress.com**

Table Of Contents

Prologue

Japan clings to a reputation for high-speed trains, robots, and futuristic cities, but that's not quite the impression you get walking past one of Japan's many DVD stores or watching someone at the office fiddling with the fax machine.

The pace of technological change in Japan can be slow but when it does occur, it tends to be premeditated and meticulously choreographed. There are several examples in Japan's rich history, but nothing compares with the country's swift transition to an industrialized powerhouse.

You might have thought the fax machine was overstaying its utility by several decades, but only 160 years ago, Japan was governed by a feudal system left over from medieval times. The drawing of the curtain on Japan's feudal era and the dismantling of the ruling samurai class in the 1860s was highly organized and efficient. Over the space of a decade, top-knot hairstyles, killing swords, and wages paid in units of rice were phased out and replaced with the steel and metal of a modern industrialized nation.

The transformation has intrigued me ever since I moved to Japan, especially as we look ahead to the future of artificial intelligence and knowledge work. The samurai class, similar to accountants, lawyers, and other knowledge workers today, were well-educated and respected members of society. Trained in combat and schooled in calligraphy, history, mathematics, and science, they enjoyed a secure and elevated social standing in Japan's social hierarchy.

For centuries, the samurai's main threat was rivalry with neighboring clans, but the sudden arrival of steam-powered ships from abroad eventually marked the advent of the Meiji Restoration, a period of rapid industrialization and westernization in Japan. Foreign powers, particularly the United States and several European countries, forced Japan to open its borders to international trade. This exposure to both Western technology and ideas spurred a revolution in Japan's economic, political, and social systems.

The samurai, previously the military and administrative elite, found their social and economic status removed from underneath them. The feudal system, which had provided them a guaranteed income and elevated status in society, was dismantled. A modern conscript army based on the Western model also replaced the samurai as the nation's defenders. Moreover, the rise of industry and commerce created new wealth and opportunities, leading to the emergence of a new class of rich merchants and industrialists.

These changes didn't happen overnight, but the transition was significant and swift in the grand scope of Japan's history. The samurai, who had enjoyed a secure position at the top of the social order for centuries, had to adapt to a new environment that no longer valued their traditional skills or recognized their social privileges.

Similar to the changes brought by modern machinery and weaponry in the 19th Century, AI poses a threat to a large and highly skilled segment of today's workforce. Despite increased globalization, knowledge workers have always found reassurance in their local knowledge, language abilities, and unique domestic expertise. However, the unfolding revolution of AI-first practices is poised to dramatically reshape the boundaries of work in ways that are difficult to foresee.

With very few precedents that we can look to for guidance, the experience of the samurai offers rare insights and valuable lessons about resilience in the face of technological change. Faced with social upheaval and technological disruption, the samurai reacted in two ways. The first approach involved rebellion and resistance, leading to violent yet ultimately futile clashes with the Emperor's technologically advanced army.

The second and more productive course of action was to embrace change and adapt to new technology. For the samurai who took this path, education played a key part. Exposure to foreign languages gave former samurai living in the port city of Nagasaki a head-start in an economy open to foreign trade and keen to learn from Western powers. The Charter Oath issued by the Emperor in 1868 stated that "knowledge shall be sought throughout the world" and those with a tongue for foreign languages were among the first to be dispatched overseas. Others stayed in Japan and leveraged their classical education to become teachers, bureaucrats, and artists in the new nation.

Re-education also played a vital role in navigating the transition to a new economy. Although the samurai had enjoyed privileged access to education (compared to merchants, farmers, and the lowest class of Japanese society), their pre-Meiji education was relegated to foundational knowledge in an evolving economy. Their classical education, though comprehensive for the time, didn't fully prepare them for the significant shifts brought about by rapid modernization and westernization. Beyond literacy and basic arithmetic, many elements of samurai training were undesirable or obsolete, especially in warfare and philosophy. Battles would now be fought with modern weaponry, and, like ancient Greek and Latin, knowledge of the Chinese analects offered marginal utility in a modern era where Western ideas on free markets, industrialization, and capitalism ran supreme. In this way, the samurai weren't prepared to prosper in the new Japan based on their education alone. Instead, they had to recalibrate and adapt to new practices and employment pathways.

The parallels to today are striking, as professional writers, lawyers, artists, and web developers find themselves needing to acquire new skills such as text prompt writing in response to the rise of generative AI technology. The speed at which AI is seeping into all aspects of modern work—from marketing to contract writing—underscores AI literacy and understanding its key strengths and weaknesses as key knowledge for the modern workforce. Just as the Meiji Restoration in Japan introduced new job titles, there will be new opportunities in what the authors of *Human + Machine: Reimagining Work in the Age of AI* call the "missing middle", the nexus or fertile space where humans and machines collaborate to exploit what each side does best. According to the missing middle theory, the most effective and cost-efficient path is to merge automated tools with the flexibility of human workers to achieve optimum results. This is similar to how chefs and waitstaff work alongside automatic cashier machines inside Japanese restaurants today.

Virtually every sector has the potential to maximize productivity and innovation by finding the right balance between human creativity, judgment, and empathy, and AI's speed, scalability, and quantitative capabilities. In the ongoing era of AI and with new tools such as ChatGPT, we aren't just bystanders but active participants. As knowledge workers, we can embrace AI as a partner in our daily tasks, optimizing our abilities and complementing our existing skills. As leaders, we can champion AI to foster a culture of innovation, driving transformation and competitive advantage inside our organizations.

These transformations won't just impact individual tasks, but entire workflows, industries, and even societies. As a result, we need to recognize and address the challenges that AI presents, including ethical considerations, job displacement concerns, and the need for re-skilling. By proactively confronting these issues, we can ensure that the rise of AI benefits more people and not only a select few.

Admittedly, this is a narrow path to walk, and this book does not hold the wisdom and solutions to a fair and symbiotic future for humans and machines. Instead, I hope to hold your hand through understanding the fundamentals of artificial intelligence and prepare you for important discussions and decisions regarding the use of AI in your organization or daily life. This includes a series of practical thought exercises dispersed over multiple chapters.

Lastly, please keep in mind that this book is aimed at non-technical readers, including marketers, product managers, entrepreneurs, and students, seeking to build or expand their understanding of artificial intelligence. While the following chapters provide a solid foundation of core AI techniques, the book does not delve into highly technical aspects or run through coding examples for building AI programs. For a more in-depth exploration of algorithms and coding prediction models using Python, you may like to read my other titles *Machine Learning for Absolute Beginners* or *Machine Learning With Python*. These books offer a more technical and detailed treatment of machine learning algorithms and will help to complement your understanding of AI gained from reading this book.

1

Introduction

Machine intelligence represents a significant milestone in human innovation and after decades of research and two AI winters, artificial intelligence now dominates mainstream attention and is promising revolutionary changes in the way we work, create, and live our lives.

While the inception of AI as a field of study can be traced back to the 1950s, it's only in recent years that this technology has formed a significant component in our daily lives. Today, it manifests in various forms, from digital assistants like Siri and Alexa to recommendation engines on TikTok, Netflix, and Amazon, as well as new content generation tools like ChatGPT and DALL-E.

Despite its growing ubiquity, AI is often misunderstood and confused with data science, which is an intersecting field based on extracting insight from data and with its own set of use cases. As a comparison, a company might use the principles of data science to uncover new insights by analyzing customer interactions and website support tickets. This process involves aggregating and examining the data to identify common customer issues, peak times for customer support queries, or correlations between support ticket volume and specific product features. Using a data science methodology, the overall goal is to be as precise as possible at identifying patterns and trends that might help to inform the company's decision-making.

Artificial intelligence, on the other hand, performs a different role that relies less on detective work and more on general intelligence. AI, for example, can be used by a company to power customer service chatbots on their website that mimic human interactions, answer simple customer questions, and refer more complex queries to human representatives. By applying artificial intelligence, the company's overall goal is to automate key parts of the customer journey, enhance efficiency, and enable 24/7 customer service support without relying solely on human capital.

As highlighted in these two examples, data science focuses on extracting insights and knowledge from raw data, whereas artificial intelligence aims to simulate and embed human intelligence into machines. However, in many cases, AI systems will leverage insight derived from data science to enable machines to learn and make intelligent decisions. It's important, therefore, to acknowledge the overlap between data science and AI, while also understanding that AI and data science remain two different approaches to solving complex problems.

Beyond data science, AI encompasses a variety of subfields and techniques including machine learning, deep learning, generative AI, natural language processing, cybernetics, and computer vision. Regardless of the methods used, artificial intelligence, at its core, returns to the overarching mission of creating systems capable of performing tasks that would normally require human intelligence. Such tasks include understanding human language, recognizing patterns, learning from experience, making informed decisions, and even displaying emotional intelligence.

Learning from experience and making informed decisions falls into the subfield of machine learning, which entails the use of statistical methods to create prediction models that improve their performance on a specific task through experience and exposure to data. An example of this can be seen in email spam filters, which learn to distinguish spam from regular emails more accurately over time.

Pattern recognition, meanwhile, forms the basis of many AI applications, from biometric identification systems that recognize fingerprints or retina patterns to recommendation systems that analyze our online shopping patterns to suggest products we are likely to buy.

Emotional intelligence in AI, while still in its nascent stage, aims to enable machines to recognize and respond to human emotions. It has potential applications in many areas such as mental health and customer service, where it's possible for AI to assist in providing assistance, empathy, and emotional support to humans.

Understanding these different use cases and the breadth of AI helps underline the fact that AI isn't one monolithic technology or technique but rather a collection of technologies and approaches that strive to emulate human intelligence. Acknowledging this diversity is crucial for appreciating the full spectrum of AI technology and recognizing the multitude of possible use cases.

The next essential insight for those keen on understanding AI further is the realization that AI is still only in its first stage of potential evolution. This first stage is known as *narrow AI* or *weak AI*, which describes systems designed to perform a narrow task, such as voice recognition or recommending relevant products. These systems excel at the specific tasks they were designed to undertake but lack the understanding or consciousness to freely apply their capabilities to other use cases.

At the same time, we are edging closer to the next stage of AI development, known as *artificial general intelligence (AGI)* or *strong AI*. AGI refers to a version of AI that possesses the ability to understand, learn, adapt, and implement its knowledge across a broad range of tasks at a comparable or superior level to that of a human being. To help grasp the concept of general AI, it's useful to think of science fiction portrayals where AI entities, like Data from Star Trek or Ava from the movie Ex Machina, mingle with humans and exhibit cognitive abilities that are indistinguishable from ours. These AI entities are often shown to possess self-awareness, emotions, creativity, and the ability to understand and exhibit human-like behaviors, which are all hallmarks of general AI.

However, as with any powerful new technology, AGI raises a selection of ethical and privacy issues that must be navigated with care, as we will discuss in later chapters. We will also look further at the three stages of AI development and explore the potential ramifications of the final stage known as superintelligent AI. Beyond that, we will explore the major subfields of AI including machine learning, deep learning, natural language processing, generative AI, recommender systems, and computer vision. The final chapter will lay down a series of tips and insights for adopting AI in your job or organization.

For now, understand that your journey into AI has many potential paths and the field will continue to evolve as we edge closer to the next stage of machine intelligence.

2

A Brief History

From its humble beginnings as a scientific curiosity to the powerful technology we now know today, AI has survived several seasons of scarcity and abundance, doubt and optimism, and fluctuating levels of government support before embarking on a path toward exponential growth. To understand where we stand currently and the future trajectory of AI, we first need to look back at the fragmented chronology of its evolution and decades-long development.

While the roots of artificial intelligence can be linked loosely to the period of classical philosophers who attempted to describe human thinking as a symbolic system (which was the original focus of AI research), the modern field of study and the terminology both emerged in the middle of the 20th Century. In 1956, the term *artificial intelligence* was introduced and formally established as a special field of research at a summer workshop held at Dartmouth College.

The idea of designing intelligent machines had fascinated scientists, mathematicians, and technology researchers in the years before the conference, including prominent British mathematician and logician Alan Turing. Considered the father of modern computing, Turing made significant contributions to computation and machine intelligence during the 1940s and 1950s. This included the Turing Test, which was designed to assess a machine's ability to exhibit intelligent behavior indistinguishable from that of a human. According to the Turing Test, a machine can be considered intelligent if it can engage in a task without being detected as a machine, such as holding a conversation with a human.

Inspired by Turing and other research developments, the Dartmouth Conference was held at Dartmouth College in Hanover, New Hampshire, in the summer of 1956. The conference was organized by John McCarthy, Marvin Minsky, Nathaniel Rochester, and Claude Shannon, four leading figures in the fields of mathematics, cognitive science, and computer engineering. Their proposal for the conference expressed an optimistic view regarding the trajectory of AI-related technology and outlined a research project that would explore the possibilities of machines imitating human intelligence. Invitations were sent to researchers known to be active and interested in the field of machine-based intelligence. The final list of participants included the four organizing members as well as notable figures such as Allen Newell and Herbert A. Simon, who all made significant contributions to AI's development.

Lacking the on-stage theatrics, sponsored booths, and free swag common at most events today, the attendees were shown their rooms and quickly put to work. Mirroring an eight-week-long hackathon, the conference's attendees spent their days attempting to build computer programs capable of imitating human intelligence. This included working on problems still considered core to the field of AI today, such as natural language processing, problem-solving, learning and adaptation, and perception.

However, perhaps the most significant outcome of the conference was the agreement on terminology and the establishment of AI as its own distinct field of study. Steered by John McCarthy, the term *artificial intelligence* replaced previous and now forgotten descriptors such as *automata studies* and *complex information processing.* This had the effect of focusing attention on the simulation and impersonation of human intelligence.

Moreover, the conference nurtured a community of researchers that helped to establish AI as a legitimate field of study and who would individually go on to become leaders in AI research. Equally important, the conference played a crucial role in securing financial backing for AI research, which was aided by the conference's optimistic outlook and the Cold War's emphasis on automation and computational technologies. This resulted in significant funding from government organizations and laid the groundwork for the rapid expansion of AI research.

The initial years following the Dartmouth Conference formed the first golden era of AI research and projected expansive optimism regarding the future of AI. Caught up in the excitement, researchers made ambitious forecasts, predicting machines would be capable of achieving complex human tasks in a matter of years.

Funding was abundant during this time and AI research centers sprung up at prestigious universities across the United States including Stanford University, MIT, and Carnegie Mellon. The crux of AI research centered on rule-based systems as researchers attempted to encode human knowledge and intelligence into machines as a set of logical rules, which later gave birth to the development of expert systems in the 1970s and early 1980s.

By design, expert systems operate under a collection of predefined rules that generate a recommendation such as a medical diagnosis through a sequence of decisions. Commonly structured as "if-then" statements, fixed rules are set such as "if the patient has a fever above 38°C, then they may have an infection" and "if the patient has a rash and has been exposed to poison ivy, then they may have contact dermatitis". By stacking a series of if-then statements, an expert system can be designed to analyze a patient's medical history and symptoms in order to provide a potential diagnosis or propose additional tests and treatments.

While these systems are capable of performing well at narrow and well-defined tasks, they are largely flawed as an effective long-term solution. Firstly, they rely on the expertise and manual input of human professionals to contribute knowledge to the system. Translating this knowledge into a structured format of rules demands significant time and effort, which means that expert systems lack the ability to learn autonomously. Moreover, as knowledge and expertise evolve over time, these systems depend on regular updates in order to remain current and accurate. The net result is a system that is expensive and resource-intensive to build and maintain. What's more, failure to keep the system up to date carries the risk of an outdated or incorrect diagnosis or recommendation.

The next problem is the domain specificity of these systems. Their design and rule base are tailored to solving specific problems, making it difficult to transfer these systems across tasks. Deploying expert systems in different contexts requires substantial modifications or, in most cases, the development of entirely new systems. Even when deployed within a specific context, the contextual understanding of expert systems is severely limited. Operating within the constraints of predefined rules, expert systems struggle to grasp the broader context or interpret information that is outside their explicit rule library. This lack of adaptability and flexibility poses real challenges, especially when facing complex, ambiguous, or special scenarios that require nuanced judgment.

Over time, these challenges became increasingly apparent, along with the obvious failure of artificial intelligence to deliver on the ambitious promises made by AI researchers. By the mid-1970s, many of the expected breakthroughs turned out to be more difficult than originally anticipated. Rule-based systems, which had been the primary approach to AI research up to this point, were proving expensive and time-consuming to run, and failing to replicate the nuanced and complex nature of human intelligence.

This lack of progress resulted in growing skepticism, which then spread to policymakers and led to significant funding cuts. In the United States, the government, especially the Defense Advanced Research Projects Agency (DARPA), reduced and eventually cut most of its AI research funding. In the United Kingdom, the infamous *Lighthill Report*, published in 1973, critically assessed the lack of progress made by AI research, which resulted in cuts in government support for AI research at many British institutions.

Broad funding cuts prompted the beginning of the end for numerous AI projects and interest in the field dwindled across the broader AI research community. This period of deflated funding and interest, starting from the mid-1970s and extending into the early 1980s, became known as "AI winter". Used to describe a period of disillusionment and fall-off in AI funding, the term is a takeoff on the idea of a "nuclear winter", a dark period marred by coldness and barrenness.

Despite the challenging circumstances, a dedicated group of AI researchers persisted and continued their work throughout this period, with their efforts eventually leading to a resurgence in interest over the subsequent decade. The evolution of machine learning in the 1980s marked a pivotal transformation in the landscape of AI research. Instead of attempting to encode knowledge as a set of predefined rules, machine learning proposed the notion that computers could learn from data, identify patterns, and make decisions with minimal human involvement. While the theoretical foundations of machine learning had been established in earlier decades, research funding and general interest had, until this point, been channeled into expert systems.

This shift breathed new life into the AI research community. The pivot, however, was not instant but rather a gradual process driven by a series of breakthroughs and milestones. One of the critical milestones during this period was the application of an algorithm technique called backpropagation. Short for "backward propagation of errors", backpropagation significantly improves the efficiency of multi-layer neural networks. It enables the model to adjust its internal parameters in response to the difference between its actual output and the desired output, thereby improving the model's accuracy through a series of iterations. While multi-layer neural networks and the concept of backpropagation existed prior to the 1980s, their applicability was limited due to computational constraints. The increasing power of computers in the 1980s made it feasible to train larger neural networks, opening up new possibilities for the application of machine learning.

The increasing availability of digital data during this period also benefited machine learning. As computers became more prevalent in business, academia, and government, large volumes of data began to accumulate. With large datasets needed to learn patterns effectively, demand for machine learning began to build. This combination of computational power, algorithmic innovation, and data availability set the stage for the application of machine learning across a broad range of research projects, from speech recognition and computer vision to medical diagnosis. By the end of the 1980s, machine learning had firmly established itself as the leading approach in AI research, but this return to optimism would again prove harmful. Just as volcanic lava can shoot high into the air before it starts to fall or an athlete's career can reach its peak before it starts to decline, there's inevitably a peak in AI development where doom presents itself as a triumph in disguise.

Repeating patterns of the past, the next downturn was caused by a variety of factors, spanning inflated expectations, technical challenges, and economic pressures. Despite various technological advancements, machine learning models were still costly and slow to run. What's more, the hype surrounding AI again led to inflated expectations that the present technology failed to live up to. When these expectations weren't met, both investors and the public pulled back their support, leading to a decrease in funding and interest, similar to the outbreak of the first AI winter.

The economic conditions of the time played a role too. The conclusion of the Cold War in 1991 prompted large cuts in defense spending, which impacted funding for AI research, and a recession in the early 1990s tightened budgets both in industry and academia, further reducing resources available for AI research. Still, research into AI and machine learning persisted throughout this period, albeit at a slower pace than the years prior. The experience of a second AI winter led researchers to adopt a more measured approach to their work, with a focus on specific and solvable problems as well as making more realistic claims about AI's capabilities.

As the 1990s rolled on, the rise of the Internet helped set the stage for the next wave of development as vast amounts of digital data became available. Interest and funding in AI started to rebound by the late 1990s and early 2000s, thanks in part to some technical advances and the growing importance of digital data. The success of AI systems across a variety of tasks, ranging from chess competitions to speech recognition, helped improve AI's brand image and rebuild confidence in the field. This included IBM Deep Blue's win over Garry Kasparov to become the first AI system to defeat a reigning world chess champion.

By the turn of the millennium, AI was on a path of steady growth and development. The emergence of new algorithms in the early 2000s for solving classification problems and a series of practical demonstrations helped to reinforce AI's credibility and illustrate the real-world applicability of AI systems. This included a defining moment in the field of AI robotics after Stanford's autonomous car, Stanley, won the 2005 DARPA Grand Challenge by driving 131 miles across the desert without direct human intervention.

However, the real revolution was still brewing and one that would push the boundaries of AI capabilities closer to reality. The late 2000s, more than anything else, marked a leap forward in deep learning, a subfield of machine learning and another example of AI theory well ahead of its time. The concepts and principles of deep learning have their roots in the 1980s but remained unrealized for several decades. Once again, this wasn't necessarily a shortcoming of the theory but rather a limitation of the technology available.

Deep learning, named so for its use of "deep" networks with many layers of decision-making, describes a unique way of learning from complex data. In deep learning, multiple layers of decision-making are used to calculate a progressively more abstract representation than the previous one. However, even with well-defined structures and algorithms, such as backpropagation for error correction, the computational demands for training these complex networks remained outside what was technically possible.

Geoffrey Hinton, often referred to as the godfather of deep learning, became a key figure in the development of deep learning during the mid-2000s. He advocated the idea that simple learning algorithms, when fed a sufficient amount of data and computed with sufficient processing power, could surpass traditional hand-coded software. Hilton's big breakthrough came in 2006 when he introduced a more efficient way to train deep neural networks—a concept that paved the way for practical applications of deep learning.

Hilton's breakthroughs were followed by two distinct but equally vital developments: the ongoing surge of big data and the advent of powerful graphics processing units (known as GPUs). In regard to the former, the ongoing penetration and acceleration of the Internet and the digital age brought with it an unprecedented supply of data. Smartphones, social media, e-commerce, and various other digital channels contributed to a vast and ever-growing reservoir of data. Deep learning models, which learn by adjusting their parameters to minimize prediction errors, perform more effectively when exposed to large amounts of data. The big data era, therefore, provided the perfect environment for these data-hungry models.

However, vast data alone could not solve the computational bottleneck. Training deep learning models involves complex calculations and adjustments across millions, if not billions, of different parameters. This is where GPUs, originally designed for video games and computer graphics, caught the eye of AI researchers. In contrast to traditional central processing units (CPUs) that undertake calculations one after the other, graphics processing units are engineered to perform multiple computations concurrently, which enables a more sophisticated and immersive graphics experience.

Investment in GPU technology exploded and by 2005, mass production strategies drove the costs of these chips down substantially. This price reduction, paired with their unique processing capabilities, expanded the potential applications for GPUs beyond the realm of graphics rendering, paving the way for their use in other fields including deep learning and, later, Bitcoin mining.

In the case of deep learning, the advantage of GPUs lies in their ability for parallel processing. This capability aligns with the demands of deep learning computations, which are predominantly matrix and vector operations. The capacity of GPUs to handle these calculations concurrently, rather than sequentially, attracted the interest of researchers including Andrew Ng[1]. As a professor at Stanford University, Ng's experiments with GPUs led to significant reductions in training times for deep learning models, making it feasible to build more complex neural networks. This development signaled a paradigm shift, with deep learning models outperforming traditional AI approaches across numerous tasks including image and speech recognition as well as natural language processing. The advancements in deep learning led by Ng and other researchers including Geoffrey Hinton in the area of backpropagation pushed the boundaries of what was thought possible, with their findings facilitating new breakthroughs and startups including DeepMind and OpenAI.

Acquired by Google in 2014, DeepMind is best known for developing AlphaGo, a deep learning program that defeated the world champion in the game of Go 2016. Due to the complexity and intuitive nature of the game, the feat

---

[1] It's important to note that Andrew Ng's contributions to deep learning stretch beyond his work with GPUs. His popular Coursera course on machine learning has introduced millions of students worldwide to AI. His tenure at Google Brain, meanwhile, led to the development of large-scale deep neural networks, pushing the boundaries of what was thought possible.

was considered a major milestone in AI, and the publicity generated from the five-match series fueled a flood of interest in deep learning among students and startups. The company has since ventured into using AI to tackle societal challenges, such as the protein folding problem in biology and forecasting energy production for wind farms.

OpenAI, meanwhile, has made headlines with the release of generative AI products including DALL-E and ChatGPT that are capable of generating unique art and performing knowledge-based tasks such as translation, question answering, and summarizing text. These recent advancements introduced by OpenAI are set to form an integral part of many sectors and industries, driving innovations in areas such as education, marketing, entertainment, web development, and visual design.

As we delve deeper in the following chapters, we will look closer at how generative AI and other examples of AI work, as well as their common applications and the potential AI holds for the future.

Key Takeaways

1) The history of AI has experienced a recurring pattern of inflated expectations and hibernation periods known as *AI winters*, characterized by periods of decreased funding and interest. These different cycles highlight the importance of maintaining realistic expectations and a measured approach to AI's capabilities.

2) The resilience of AI, seen throughout its history, can be partly attributed to the Lindy effect, which suggests that the longer an idea or technology survives, the longer its future life expectancy becomes. AI's ability to overcome periods of skepticism, funding cuts, and technological limitations underlines its resilience and reinforces the notion that the longer AI continues to advance, the more likely it is here to stay.

3) The advent of powerful graphics processing units played a crucial role in the modern era of AI by enabling the parallel processing required for complex computations. This ability significantly reduces the time to train a model

and has facilitated the development of deep learning, pushing the boundaries of what AI can achieve.

Thought Exercise

1) What percentage of the current AI cycle do you think is hype or exaggerated? What aspects of AI aren't hype and how can you focus on these opportunities?

3

AI Building Blocks

Just as physical laws govern the mechanics of the universe, the field of artificial intelligence is controlled and regulated by algorithms. They underpin the advanced capabilities we see today, from the more simple act of recommending a song based on a user's listening history, to the complex task of driving an autonomous vehicle.

By definition, algorithms are sets of specific instructions designed to perform a task or solve a problem. They are the essential building blocks and the recipe for every good AI system. But unlike recipes written in human language, these algorithms are written in code and read by machines. While explaining the code and mathematical intricacies of popular algorithms is beyond the scope of this book, the following chapter provides a high-level overview of different algorithm categories, including classification, regression, sorting, and clustering techniques, as well as transparent and black box algorithms.

First, let's examine the shared characteristics of algorithms within the context of artificial intelligence. Fundamentally, algorithms function by processing data inputs to yield an output. Input data can include text, images, audio, video, sensor data, or any other form of unprocessed information. For a recommendation engine, the output might be a series of suggested products, and for a facial recognition system, the output might be an identification or face match.

AI algorithms typically have the capacity to learn and improve over time. As more data is processed, the algorithm fine-tunes its understanding, often improving the quality of its outputs. This feedback typically comes in the form of a loss function, a measure of how well the algorithm is performing its task. The loss function quantifies the difference between the algorithm's actual output and the expected output. Lower values of the loss function imply better performance.

When the loss function indicates that the output is failing to achieve what was expected, the algorithm undergoes an optimization process. This process involves adjusting the internal parameters of the algorithm to better align its outputs with the expected result. In essence, this is the algorithm's way of learning from its past mistakes. Parameters, meanwhile, are the internal settings that the algorithm adjusts during the optimization process. The exact nature and number of these parameters depend on the specific algorithm being used. An example of an algorithm with very few parameters is the k-nearest neighbors (k-NN) algorithm. In k-NN, the number of parameters is determined by the value of k, which represents the number of nearest neighbors used for classification or regression. Conversely, an artificial neural network may consist of thousands of different parameters.

Classification vs. Regression

It's essential to understand that there's no one-size-fits-all algorithm when it comes to AI. Different algorithms cater to different tasks and different types of data. The choice of algorithm depends on the specific problem you are attempting to solve.

To illustrate, classification algorithms are designed to assign the input data to a certain category or class based on its features, such as identifying whether an email is spam and whether a tumor is malignant or benign. The task of classifying instances is conducted by analyzing the characteristics or composition of existing examples and then creating a prediction model that captures relationships between the features and the class labels in order to predict the class of instances yet to be classified. This could involve diagnosing whether a patient is carrying a specific

26

disease, such as diabetes, based on different health indicators. In this scenario, the output or class label is binary: "diabetes" or "no diabetes". The explanatory features include a range of health measurements such as patients' blood pressure, body mass index (BMI), age, cholesterol levels, and so on. These measurements are collected from a large number of patients, some of whom have been diagnosed with diabetes and some who have not. This data is then used to train a classification model.

Patient ID	Blood Pressure	BMI	Age	Cholesterol Levels	Diabetes
1	120/80	25.3	40	180	No
2	140/90	29.8	55	220	Yes
3	130/85	27.6	65	200	Yes
4	118/75	22.1	32	150	No
5	150/95	31.2	48	240	Yes

Table 1: Sample data for classification of patients with diabetes

The training process involves feeding the features and the corresponding class labels ("diabetes" and "no diabetes") of each patient into the algorithm. The algorithm will analyze these features and establish a relationship between them and the corresponding class labels to create a trained model that captures these relationships. The trained model can then be used to predict the likelihood of a patient having diabetes based on the input of their health measurements.

When a new patient's data is fed into the model, the model can classify them as having "diabetes" or "no diabetes" based on the relationships it learned from the training data. For instance, the model may have learned that patients over the age of 50 with a high BMI and high blood pressure are statistically more likely to have diabetes. Thus, if a new patient matches that criteria, the model will classify the patient in the "diabetes" category. However, it's important to remember that the model is actually making an estimate based on the data it was trained on, and while this can be highly accurate, certain errors are unavoidable, especially if the model doesn't account for fringe cases.

Regression algorithms, on the other hand, are used to predict continuous values (in numerical terms, i.e. 5, 4, 5.4, etc.), such as evaluating the value of a house or predicting a patient's life expectancy. In the case of the second example, the explanatory variables can include a range of the same health measurements used in the previous example, such as blood pressure, body mass index (BMI), age, and cholesterol levels. The difference is that the target outcome is no longer binary ("diabetes" and "no diabetes") but a continuous value: the patient's life expectancy measured in years. The dataset again comprises numerous examples of patients, each characterized by their feature values in terms of health measurements but instead, there is a new column with a life expectancy value expressed in numbers.

Patient ID	Blood Pressure	BMI	Age	Cholesterol Levels	Diabetes	Life Expectancy
1	120/80	25.3	40	180	No	78
2	140/90	29.8	55	220	Yes	72
3	130/85	27.6	65	200	Yes	68
4	118/75	22.1	32	150	No	82
5	150/95	31.2	48	240	Yes	65

Table 2: Sample data for regression of patient's life expectancy

A regression algorithm, such as linear regression, can then be trained on the dataset to create a model. The training process involves feeding the features and corresponding life expectancy values of each patient into the algorithm. The algorithm will then analyze those features and establish a relationship between the explanatory variables and life expectancy, which is the target variable for this model.

Once the training phase is complete, the algorithm will have learned and designed a model that can predict the life expectancy of a patient. When a new patient's data is entered into the model, the model estimates their life expectancy based on their specific health measurements. For instance, the model might have learned that patients who are younger, with a lower BMI, and who have controlled blood pressure tend to enjoy a higher life expectancy. Therefore, if a new patient's data fits these criteria, the model will estimate a higher life expectancy for that patient. However, similar to the classification model example, the model's prediction constitutes an estimation based on a generalization of the data the model was trained on and is not guaranteed to be 100% correct and the model may need to be retrained over time.

In summary, classification and regression algorithms are designed to handle different types of problems. Classification is used when the target variable is a category or a class, such as "spam" or "not spam" in the case of email filtering. Regression is used when the target variable is a real or continuous value, like house prices measured in dollars or life expectancy measured in years.

For a deeper exploration of specific classification and regression algorithms, I have documented these techniques in a separate book, *Machine Learning for Absolute Beginners: Third Edition*, which walks through the process of designing basic prediction models.

Sorting & Clustering

In addition to classification and regression, there are also sorting and clustering algorithms.

Sorting algorithms arrange a collection of items or data points in a specific order, making it easier to analyze. Sorting can be performed on various types of data, including numbers, dates, and strings. For example, consider a list of numbers: [11, 23, 1, 5, 2]. By applying a sorting algorithm, such as merge sort, the list can be rearranged in ascending order: [1, 2, 5, 11, 23].

Clustering, on the other hand, involves grouping similar data points together based on shared characteristics or similarities. The objective is to identify patterns, structures, or relationships within the data without any predefined labels or categories. Spam email, for example, isn't usually labeled by the sender as "spam", but by grouping emails together based on the subject line, contents, and external links, it's possible to group most of the spam email messages into a cluster based on similar patterns—all without any labels directly categorizing these emails as "spam".

Another common example of clustering is finding customers who share similar purchasing patterns. By identifying a cluster of customers who share purchasing preferences, such as time of purchase and seasonal factors, brands can identify distinct customer segments for targeted marketing campaigns.

Algorithm Transparency

In addition to matching the model with the type of problem you are attempting to solve, you also need to consider the model's interpretability. To elaborate, some algorithms are relatively easy to understand but might not always be the most accurate. Other algorithms can be highly accurate but are often described as black boxes because their internal decision-making process is difficult to interpret.

Transparent or highly interpretable algorithms are those where the steps taken to produce an output are easy to follow and clear to interpret. Decision trees and linear regression are two examples of algorithms where the relationship between the input(s) and the output is clear and easy to follow. The logic behind these algorithms can be examined step by step, allowing you to understand correlations and the specific variables that led to the final output. In general, transparent algorithms are useful in contexts where understanding the reasoning behind decisions is crucial, such as a credit loan decision or house valuation.

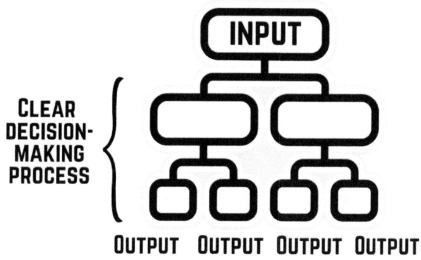

CLEAR
DECISION-
MAKING
PROCESS

INPUT

OUTPUT   OUTPUT   OUTPUT   OUTPUT

Figure 1: Decision tree

Black box algorithms, on the other hand, are those where the pathway from input to output cannot be easily traced or explained. Examples of black box algorithms are multi-layered neural networks. These models involve layers and layers of interconnected neurons that process input data, transforming it multiple times to reach an output. Due to the large number of transformations and the non-linear nature of these transformations, it's extremely difficult to understand how a neural network makes its decision. This lack of transparency can become problematic in contexts where accountability and explainability are needed or favored.

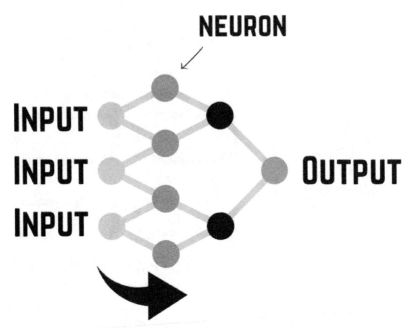

Figure 2: Basic 4-layer feed-forward neural network

Balancing the need for highly effective AI systems and the need for transparency and accountability is a key issue in AI research and ethics. The development of techniques to improve the interpretability of black box models, a field known as *explainable AI*, is an active area of study seeking to address this issue. Explainable AI refers to the ability of an AI system to provide understandable explanations or justifications for its decisions and actions. In medical diagnosis, for example, explainable AI can help to provide doctors with clear explanations of how a system arrived at a diagnosis or treatment recommendation. This helps doctors validate the AI's suggestions and gain insights into the underlying factors considered by the model.

Datasets

Creating effective AI systems is not just about selecting and implementing the right algorithm. The design process also requires a deep understanding of the dataset the algorithm will consume and analyze.

Just as a car needs petrol or electricity to move, AI algorithms need data to learn. However, the relationship between AI and data goes beyond necessity. Understanding the nuances of data—its collection, interpretation, and limitations—is paramount to not only the effectiveness of AI systems but also fairness and transparency. Poor quality or biased data can lead to poor or biased results, a common challenge in AI called "garbage in, garbage out".

As organized stores of data, datasets provide the fuel for algorithms to operate. In the case of supervised learning (explored further in Chapter 5), a dataset is split into training and test portions with a 70:30 or 60:40 split. The training data is used to create the model, while the test data is used to evaluate the model's performance.

The quality and size of the dataset significantly impact the accuracy and reliability of the AI model. The better the dataset, the better the model's ability to learn and generalize to new inputs. Yet, datasets are not as straightforward as they might seem. Datasets can present numerous challenges that, if not properly managed, can lead to poor or erroneous predictions. A dataset that lacks diversity or that is not representative of the problem at hand can lead to models that are biased or that perform poorly when faced with real-world data.

One problem is the *curse of dimensionality*. Coined by Richard Bellman in the late 1950s, the term refers to various challenges that arise when analyzing datasets with hundreds or thousands of variables—a phenomenon that only occurs in high-dimensional datasets (with a large number of variables). According to this theory, to obtain a statistically sound and reliable result, the amount of data needed to support the result often grows exponentially with the dimensionality or number of variables analyzed. However, having too many variables also injects noise that makes it harder to identify patterns and build an accurate model. What's more, given the sheer volume of variables thrown at the model, it's possible for one or more variables to correlate with the target output due to coincidence rather than pure causation.

As anyone working in this industry will tell you, correlation does not imply causation. Just because two variables move together does not mean that one causes the other to move and the website Spurious Correlations (www.tylervigen.com/spurious-correlations) presents numerous examples of variables that are strongly correlated but clearly have no causal relationship. For instance, one chart on the site visualizes a strong correlation between the divorce rate in the state of Maine and the yearly per capita consumption of margarine in the United States. As amusing as it is to think about why this might be true, there is no reason to believe that these two trends have any effect on each other. The correlation is most likely a coincidence.

Next, the costs associated with processing large amounts of data must be taken into consideration. While having more data often improves the predictive ability of machine learning models, it amplifies computational requirements and increases model complexity. Conversely, too little data can result in models that are inadequately trained and perform poorly on new data.

Another crucial aspect is the cleanliness and integrity of the dataset. Inaccurate or missing data can significantly impair the model's performance, leading to incorrect predictions. Hence, a substantial part of building a model involves preprocessing and cleaning data to ensure its quality and consistency. This step involves filling in missing data, removing duplicates, correcting inconsistencies, converting non-numerical variables to numeric variables, and normalizing variables to maintain a consistent scale (i.e., all variables measured in "minutes" and not in multiple different units of time). It's a demanding task, but the value it brings to the model and its outputs cannot be overstated.

To demonstrate the range of data quality considerations, let's examine an example from an e-commerce company developing a machine learning model for its new marketing campaign. The aim of the model is to predict customer responses based on various variables such as past purchases, customer information, and website browsing behavior.

First, the accuracy of the data is paramount. If the past purchase history of a customer is recorded inaccurately, the predictive model might target the wrong customers and waste resources on customers who are less likely to purchase.

Completeness is the next essential aspect of data quality. If data concerning customer responses to past campaigns or seasonal events are missing, the model may not have sufficient information to make accurate predictions. This is akin to trying to complete a puzzle without all the pieces available.

Consistency in data is also crucial. Picture a scenario where the age of the customer is recorded in years in one part of the system and in months in another. Such inconsistency could lead to confusion and result in errors in the model.

The reliability of the data collected is yet another vital component of data quality. If the browsing data is collected inaccurately due to a bug in the tracking code or acquired from an unreliable third party, the model might skew its predictions. A customer might be misclassified as not being interested in certain products when they actually are, leading to inappropriate targeting and a missed sales opportunity.

Timeliness, the next metric, ensures that the model is based on the current reality. If the most recent purchase data is not updated in real time, the model could base its predictions on outdated information. For instance, a customer who recently made several baby product purchases might be incorrectly classified as unlikely to respond to a new baby product recommendation if their latest transactions aren't included in the data. Conversely, marketing to a customer who made baby product purchases five years ago may no longer be a reliable candidate for purchasing that line of products.

Relevance of the data to the task at hand is essential to avoid confusion and the waste of computational resources.

For example, including data such as the customer's phone carrier or the color of the last item purchased (if color isn't relevant to the campaign), introduces noise into the model and distracts the model from more relevant variables.

Lastly, granularity refers to the level of detail in the data. While highly detailed data might seem advantageous, it can also introduce noise into the model, leading to a problem known as overfitting where the model over-emphasizes randomness or insignificant patterns in the data. For instance, if website browsing data is recorded for every single page view, it might add unnecessary complexity without providing significant value. Conversely, if data is aggregated or too coarse (having a low level of detail), critical details about customer behavior might be overlooked and wasted.

To summarize, data is a critical asset for creating AI systems, providing the necessary information for these systems to learn, improve, and generate accurate predictions or insights. Each piece of data is like a brick used to construct a building. If the bricks are weak or flawed, the resulting building might be unstable. Similarly, if data is inaccurate, incomplete, or unreliable, the resulting AI system could produce misleading results, leading to poor decisions and potential risks. As such, a thorough understanding of data and its various aspects is indispensable when working with AI. This includes not only the ability to analyze data and check for spurious relationships but also to clean and preprocess the input data.

Quality Metric	Description	Marketing Model Example
Accuracy	The data correctly represents the entities it is describing.	Customers' purchase history is not recorded accurately due to errors in the transaction logging system.
Completeness	Complete datasets contain few or no omissions.	Data missing for customers' responses to past campaigns or missing information about customer demographics.
Consistency	Data should be consistent across different data sources and over time.	The age of customers is recorded in years in one part of the system and in months in another.
Reliability	Reliable data should be trusted and from reliable sources.	Customer data acquired from a third-party may be partly or fully fabricated.
Timeliness	Data should be available when it is needed.	Purchase data that is not updated regularly or when there's a delay between collection and model training.
Relevance	Data should be related to the task at hand.	Irrelevant data, such as customers' phone carrier, wastes computational resources and confuses the model.
Granularity	Data needs to have the right level of detail or summarization. Data that's too granular might contain more noise than signal.	If website browsing data is too coarse, such as only recording one activity per day, the model might miss important details about the customer.

Table 3: Data quality considerations and examples

AI Hardware & Software

In this next section, we'll explore the vital role that hardware and software play in facilitating artificial intelligence.

Let's start with the hardware. High-performance hardware is a cornerstone of AI, particularly in the realm of machine learning and deep learning, where vast quantities of data are the norm. From the central processing units that serve as the brains of the computer to the graphics processing units that accelerate computations, the role of hardware is to provide the raw power needed to process and run complex algorithms on the data.

CPUs vs. GPUs

During the early stages of AI development, computations were executed using CPUs, which are known for being versatile and capable of executing a variety of tasks. In practice, CPUs are used for performing sequential processing, where each instruction is executed one after another.

While CPUs are efficient for general computing tasks, advanced AI and particularly deep learning require the processing of complex mathematical operations on very large datasets, which necessitates parallel rather than sequential processing. Although originally designed to handle the rendering of pixel-rich images in computer games and gaming consoles such as the PlayStation 2 and Xbox, GPUs are specifically designed for parallel processing, which refers to the ability to perform multiple calculations at the same time. This makes them well-suited for tasks that require a lot of computing power, such as graphics processing and machine learning. This also explains why the use of GPUs in AI has become so widespread and why the production and price of GPUs are carefully monitored by companies and governments.

In general, GPUs are more expensive than CPUs to produce. The specific pricing of GPUs is influenced by multiple factors including production costs, demand, technological advancements, and geopolitics. Over time, as with many technologies, we have witnessed a general trend of price deflation in the cost per unit of computing power. This doesn't mean that the price of a GPU has decreased, but rather, that the cost for a certain level of performance (measured in floating point operations per second) has generally gone down over time. This is due to improvements in manufacturing, increased efficiency, and technological upgrades.

Nonetheless, it's important to note that the price of chips can be vulnerable to short-term fluctuations. During periods of increased interest in cryptocurrencies, the demand for chips can spike, leading to increased costs. Similarly, disruptions in the supply chain, such as those caused by the global pandemic or international trade disputes, can impact the availability and cost of computing resources.

As a byproduct of semiconductors[2], chips are becoming increasingly subject to trade war sanctions. In September

---

[2] A semiconductor is a material that has electrical conductivity between that of a conductor and an insulator. GPUs, meanwhile, are made of semiconductor

2022, the U.S. Department of Commerce added seven Chinese supercomputing entities to the Entity List, which restricts the export of certain goods and technologies to those entities. While aimed at preventing China from using chips for military purposes, the ban has far-reaching implications for the AI industry.

Specifically, the ban affects the export of chips to China from two major chipmakers, Nvidia from Taiwan and Advanced Micro Devices (AMD) from the United States. Both companies had been supplying chips, including GPUs, to China for use in supercomputers but were forced to halt shipments in response to the ban. This now makes it challenging for companies in China to obtain the GPUs they need for building AI applications. The Chinese Government has responded to the ban by imposing its own restrictions on the export of chips to the United States, making it more difficult for U.S. companies to obtain chips from China. The trade war has also prompted countries to increase their investment in local chip manufacturing, which may lead to the development of new chip innovations, supply lines, and manufacturing processes.

To learn more about the lead-up and the potential trajectory of the recent chip war, you may like to read *Chip Wars: The Fight for the World's Most Critical Technology* by Chris Miller, which tells the story of the global semiconductor industry and the growing competition between the United States and China to dominate this critical resource.

TPUs

Beyond CPUs and GPUs, there is another important type of chip to discuss. As the field of AI has advanced, more specialized hardware has been required and this has led to the development of Tensor Processing Units (TPUs), originally developed by Google.

---

materials, such as silicon, and use semiconductor devices, such as transistors, to perform their calculations.

TPUs are a type of application-specific integrated circuit (ASIC) developed specifically for accelerating machine learning workloads. They are named after the tensor data structure, which refers to a multi-dimensional array or data structure with multiple variables. The first generation of TPUs was announced in 2016 and used internally at Google to improve the efficiency and speed of their machine learning systems such as Google Search and Google Translate.

Google announced its second-generation TPU in 2017. These units were made available to external developers via Google's public cloud platform, which continues to release new and more powerful TPU generations. Other companies including Microsoft and Amazon Web Services (AWS) have followed in offering TPU services on the cloud. This has helped to accelerate the development of AI as these processing chips make it possible to train and run models on a much larger scale.

In terms of hardware comparison, while CPUs are used to handle a variety of general computing tasks and GPUs are designed to quickly process the mathematical calculations needed for rendering graphics, TPUs are specifically built to handle the kind of matrix-based computations that are common in machine learning and deep learning.

One of the significant differences between GPUs and TPUs lies in their architecture. GPUs are designed to handle a large number of relatively small computational cores for parallel processing, which is great for graphics rendering and beneficial for certain types of machine learning tasks. TPUs, on the other hand, are designed around a large matrix multiply unit, which offers high computational capability and reduced computational precision (such as lower-bit floating-point numbers) that is typically acceptable for neural network workloads. This precision reduction can still deliver accurate results for neural network models while offering significant performance gains, which makes TPUs efficient at executing the large-scale matrix operations that are often found in deep learning algorithms. TPUs can also be significantly faster than GPUs in regards to the running of machine learning applications and, in general, are more energy efficient.

However, it's crucial to note that while individual operations may be more efficient, the overall environmental impact of TPUs and GPUs raises a reason for concern. First, the manufacturing of these high-performance chips requires a lot of upfront energy and resources, including the mining of raw materials, such as silicon and rare earth metals, which are energy-intensive to mine. They then continue to consume a lot of energy once put into use. The energy consumption of these chips can be significant, especially in data centers where they are used in large quantities.

As a result, there are a number of initiatives underway to reduce the environmental impact of high-performance chips, such as the development of more energy-efficient manufacturing processes, the recycling and reusing of chips, and the use of renewable energy sources, including solar and wind power, to power data centers.

Regarding manufacturing processes, there are a number of new energy-efficient manufacturing processes being implemented including 3D stacking, which involves vertically attaching three or sometimes four chips to make better use of available chip space.

Software

Having discussed the evolution and importance of hardware, including the use of GPUs and TPUs, let's shift our focus to another critical component of AI systems: the software. AI software ranges from the programming languages used to write algorithms, such as Python and R, to specialized libraries like TensorFlow, PyTorch, and Keras that offer pre-built functions for creating and training prediction models.

(Please note that this section delves into more technical aspects, including descriptions of common code libraries. If you aren't interested in the programming side of AI, feel free to skim or skip over this section.)

Libraries

Libraries, in the context of AI software, are collections of pre-written code that developers can use to streamline their work. They span everything from simple data-importing commands to complex mathematical functions. Essentially, they provide a way to perform tasks without having to write custom code from scratch every single time you want to do something. To explain why this is important, let's consider the case of creating a neural network. Without code libraries, a programmer would need to manually code the entire architecture of the network, implement the mathematical operations for forward propagation (where the network makes its predictions) and backpropagation (where the network learns from its errors), and handle the optimization process that tweaks the network parameters for improved performance. Not only is this process extremely time-consuming but it also requires a deep understanding of the underlying mathematics.

Libraries reduce much of this complexity. When creating a neural network using TensorFlow or Keras, developers can build a model by simply stacking together pre-defined layers. Each layer might represent a set of neurons in the network, and come pre-packaged with the necessary mathematical operations. Furthermore, these libraries come with pre-implemented algorithms for training and optimizing the model. When data is fed into the model, the library takes care of passing it through the mathematical operations defined by the network's architecture, adjusting the network's weights based on the errors it makes, and iteratively improving the model. The end result is that with just a few lines of code, developers can create, train, and implement a model without having to manually insert the underlying math.

These libraries also provide code for preprocessing data, which is a critical step in creating a model. They can handle tasks like normalizing data to ensure that variables are expressed on a common scale, converting categorical variables into numerical variables, and splitting datasets into training and test sets, among other things.

Lastly, libraries play an essential role in promoting consistency and standardization. By using libraries, developers adhere to a set of standardized practices, which reduces the risk of errors and improves the replicability of the code for future use.

Beyond TensorFlow, PyTorch, and Keras, there is an extensive selection of useful libraries out there. Scikit-learn, for instance, offers a broad array of machine learning algorithms and tools for data preprocessing and model evaluation using Python. Natural Language Toolkit (NLTK) provides resources for tasks in natural language processing, a field of AI focused on the interaction between computers and human language. Matplotlib is a widely used library for creating static, animated, and interactive visualizations in Python, which is crucial for data exploration and presenting results.

Programming Langauges

Programming languages are fundamental in the development of AI systems. The choice of language often depends on the specific needs of a project, including factors such as the type of problem being solved, computational efficiency requirements, and the availability of relevant libraries and frameworks. Here, we'll discuss some of the most popular programming languages used within AI.

Python: Known for its simplicity and readability, Python is the most widely used programming language in AI and machine learning. Python boasts a plethora of libraries and frameworks that facilitate the development of AI applications, including TensorFlow, PyTorch, Keras, and Scikit-learn. It's also a great choice for beginners and experts.

R: If you're leaning towards statistical computing or data analysis, R is a language designed specifically for these purposes. It has a rich package ecosystem that facilitates statistical modeling and visualization, which are core components of AI and machine learning.

Java: Java is another language worth considering, particularly if you're building large-scale enterprise applications. It's platform independence and robust debugging features make it a versatile choice for AI development.

C++: Due to its high execution speed and control over system resources, C++ is often used in AI projects where performance is a crucial factor. It's typically used in parts of AI applications where low latency is required, although it may not be as easy to use as Python or R.

Julia: Julia is a high-level, high-performance language for technical computing. It provides the ease of use of Python and R, but also the performance of C++. Julia is gaining some popularity in the data science and AI communities, particularly in areas that require heavy numerical and scientific computation.

Prolog: Prolog, short for Programming in Logic, is a language often associated with artificial intelligence and computational linguistics. Its capacity to efficiently resolve problems involving relationships, especially those that involve structured data, makes it suited to certain AI applications.

LISP: Although less commonly used today, LISP is one of the oldest high-level programming languages and is closely associated with artificial intelligence research. It was widely used in AI research due to its symbolic processing capabilities, but its use has waned with the rise of more modern languages.

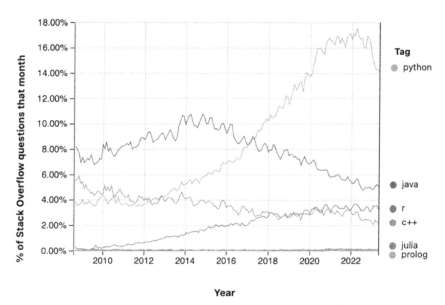

Figure 3: Percentage of Stack Overflow questions that month (not necessarily AI-specific)

The right language for a particular AI project can depend on many factors, but these languages have demonstrated their value across a wide range of AI applications. Beyond the languages themselves, you should also consider the support systems surrounding them. From tutorials and forums to sample code, an active community can be a goldmine of resources. These resources can dramatically accelerate your learning and provide much-needed support when you encounter problems with your code. Languages with large communities also tend to be regularly updated with new features and improvements, keeping you at the forefront of AI development.

The nature of your project will play a significant role in your decision too. If you are developing an AI solution that needs to integrate with existing systems, your choice might be influenced by the languages these systems use and their compatibility. Similarly, if your work involves large volumes of data, you should look for languages with strong data-handling capabilities.

Lastly, bear in mind that many AI tasks can be significantly accelerated by running them on multiple processors simultaneously. This is especially true for deep learning. As such, languages that support parallel computing can be advantageous.

In conclusion, the right language to learn for AI development depends on your personal circumstances, including your existing skills, the type of projects you intend to work on, and your performance requirements. Python, R, Java, and C++ are all excellent choices, but they come with their own strengths and weaknesses. If you are still unsure, it may be wise to default to the most popular language for AI systems, which, at this time, is Python.

Key Takeaways

1) Classification and regression are two common categories of algorithms used in AI. Classification algorithms assign input data to specific categories or classes based on their features, while regression algorithms predict continuous values.

2) Sorting algorithms arrange data into a specific order, facilitating easier understanding. Clustering algorithms, on the other hand, group similar data points together without predefined labels, allowing for the identification of new patterns and relationships.

3) Transparency and interpretability of algorithms are important considerations. Transparent algorithms have clear and understandable steps, making their decision-making process easily interpretable. Black box algorithms, on the other hand, lack transparency and their internal workings are difficult to trace.

4) Datasets play a crucial role in AI systems. The quality, diversity, and relevance of the data used to train AI models significantly impact their performance. Inaccurate, biased, or incomplete data can lead to poor or biased predictions. Preprocessing and cleaning the data are also important steps for ensuring data quality.

5) Libraries promote convenience and consistency. By using established libraries, developers adhere to standardized practices, reducing the risk of errors and improving the replicability of code for future use.

6) The choice of programming language should consider factors such as computational efficiency, library availability, community support, integration with existing systems, data handling capabilities, and parallel computing support.

7) Python is currently the most widely used language in AI and machine learning, offering simplicity, readability, and a rich ecosystem of libraries.

Thought Exercises

1) What's a real-life example reflecting the curse of dimensionality? Is there a business book, news channel, conspiracist, politician, or popular theory, for instance, that draws on a select number of seemingly correlated examples that are coincidental and not typical of the true situation?

2) Do you think classification problems or regression problems are more common in your organization or institution? (i.e., how much to pay interns is a regression problem, whereas selecting new interns based on their credentials is a classification problem.)

3) Is model transparency important for a football coach using a prediction model to recruit players who are likely to score goals? Do fans betting on a football player to score also need to know why the model predicts that player to score or is model accuracy more important?

4) Pick an industry you are currently interested in and think of a special use case for AI. Now ask whether model interpretability and transparency are important for evaluating the effectiveness of the model.

4

The 3 Stages of AI Development

As you venture further into the field of AI, it's important to recognize and understand the three potential stages of AI development. Spanning narrow AI, general AI, and superintelligent AI, these three stages represent crucial milestones in the evolution of AI technology.

Narrow AI, for example, is designed to perform a specific task, whereas general AI is more advanced and capable of understanding, learning, and applying knowledge flexibly across a broad spectrum of tasks. As the most advanced stage, superintelligent AI remains a theoretical category at present but is hypothesized to surpass human intelligence across multiple domains at some point in the future.

Narrow AI

Despite its name, *narrow AI* or *weak AI* should not be confused as weak or ineffective. Rather, the naming of this category refers to the focused nature of AI systems in relation to their scope and functionality.

By design, narrow AI systems are capable of mimicking human intelligence but are constrained to a specific domain, meaning they can't perform tasks outside of what they are trained or programmed to do. To illustrate, an AI system designed for image recognition can identify and categorize images based on its training but cannot translate languages or diagnose diseases without radical adjustments and additional training data.

This might make narrow AI seem limited in terms of application, but these specialized systems form the backbone of many powerful AI applications. Google's search engine, Amazon's recommendation engine, Apple's Siri, and Tesla's Autopilot are all examples of narrow AI systems. Each of these systems performs specific tasks exceptionally well, often surpassing human capabilities in speed, accuracy, and efficiency. Google's search engine, for instance, can process billions of web pages and deliver the most relevant search results in a fraction of a second. It's optimized to perform this specific task and outperform any human assistant. However, the same system is clueless when it comes to steering a car or writing a poem. This underlines the essence of narrow AI: exceptional at performing a specific task but inflexible and unable to operate effectively on other tasks.

General AI

Having established the definition of narrow AI, let's turn our attention to a more advanced iteration and the next phase of AI development called *general AI* or *strong AI*.

General AI, often referred to as *artificial general intelligence* or *AGI*, refers to a version of artificial intelligence that has the ability to perform any cognitive task achievable by a human. Note, however, that this definition does not encompass physical abilities or the use of robotics, which are often subject to different tests and forms of evaluation. *The Coffee Test*, proposed by Apple Co-founder Steve Wozniak, for instance, sets a benchmark for evaluating physical capabilities by testing a robot's ability to enter an unfamiliar house, find the kitchen, identify the tools and ingredients, and prepare a cup of coffee. Robots are yet to pass the test and this example is just one of many benchmarks currently in discussion regarding AGI (beyond the boundaries of solely cognitive tasks).

When it comes to cognitive tasks, benchmarks and definitions of AGI remain varied, which creates a sliding scale of standards and expectations. In general, the more specific the definition (such as the ability to converse with humans on any topic in multiple languages), the easier or lower the target of AGI becomes. Conversely, the less specific the definition (perform any task a human can do), the higher the AGI benchmark becomes. Depending on the definition, AGI might also include a biological component, physical capabilities, consciousness, or some other human quality, which comes with its own set of design challenges. Broad physical capabilities, for example, are difficult to achieve due to the lack of data available to train robots or humanoid robots. ChatGPT was trained on millions of data sources scoured from the World Wide Web but the data available to train robots is much harder to find and acquire. Consciousness, meanwhile, is the subjective feeling of being aware that one exists and having an understanding of the surrounding environment. Some experts contend that having an inner mental life is not replicable in machines because consciousness arises from biological substrates and cannot be replicated in non-biological entities.

Amidst these nuanced attempts to define general intelligence, the core of the discourse and research on AGI centers on emulating cognitive abilities across a comprehensive range of non-physical tasks. This includes the ability to reason, solve puzzles, plan, learn, integrate prior knowledge into decision-making, and communicate in a natural language such as English or Spanish. Importantly, general AI includes the ability to transfer knowledge from one domain to another—a skill known as *transfer learning*. This might involve leveraging its understanding from reading books to engage in a meaningful conversation about literature, a capability that is well beyond the ability of narrow AI systems.

It's important to highlight that as of the time of writing, general AI remains unrealized. While we've made significant strides in AI technology, we're still some way from creating a machine that can fully replicate the broad cognitive capabilities of the human mind. Most of the AI systems we have today, including GPT-4, are considered narrow AI because they excel at specific tasks (such as content generation) but don't possess a generalized understanding or ability to reason beyond their specific training. Also, while some applications are capable of performing multiple different tasks, they are actually using a collection of narrow AI models under the hood.

One candidate for driving progress in the field of general AI is AutoGPT. As an open-source AI agent powered by OpenAI's GPT-4 API, the system can generate text and perform various tasks autonomously, including code writing, language translation, text summarization, question answering, creative text generation, and online task completion. It operates by breaking down user goals into subtasks and utilizing access to apps, software, and online services to accomplish those tasks. For instance, if a user requests AutoGPT to compose a Tweet about coding, the agent will segment the task into subtasks like finding a coding tutorial, reading the tutorial, composing the Tweet, and posting it on Twitter.

Using AutoGPT, one user has created the Do Anything Machine, which is a to-do list that uses a GPT-4 agent, log-in access to the necessary services, and your personal or company information to complete each new task added to the list. Other users are using AutoGPT to research and script podcasts, conduct market research for new products, and create websites from scratch.

Although AutoGPT demonstrates promise and has the potential to serve as a robust automation tool for complex projects, it falls short of emulating human intelligence across a broad spectrum of tasks or rivaling human capabilities, including reasoning, in its current form. It's also common for AutoGPT to encounter problems or fail at fulfilling tasks, especially for more nuanced tasks. Still, it signifies a step towards the development of general AI by showcasing the feasibility of creating AI models capable of connecting to different online tools and adapting to new tasks without direct human supervision.

Superintelligent AI

Following our exploration of general AI, let us now venture into the most speculative phase of artificial intelligence. Although it currently resides within the bounds of theoretical forecasts and human imagination, superintelligent AI presents a vision of the future that has long captivated scientists, philosophers, futurists, and science fiction writers.

While general AI aims to replicate the full spectrum of human cognitive abilities, superintelligent AI goes a step further, seeking to exceed human capabilities. In theory, a superintelligent AI would not only outperform humans at any intellectual task but would also outperform humans in high-value endeavors including scientific research, strategic planning, and social influencing. Thus, the idea of superintelligent AI extends beyond an advanced tool or system; it suggests a potentially autonomous entity capable of out-thinking humanity and coming up with ideas, strategies, and solutions that exceed the abilities of the smartest human minds. As such, it raises questions and concerns about control and alignment with human values that are significantly more challenging than those associated with general AI.

This leads us to what's termed the *control problem*, a term popularized by philosopher Nick Bostrom, author of the seminal book *Superintelligence: Paths, Dangers, Strategies*. The control problem refers to the theoretical difficulty of controlling or restraining a superintelligent AI. If AI surpasses human intelligence, it might become impossible to fully predict or control its actions. The AI entity could devise strategies to avoid being shut down or it could manipulate humans in ways we are unable to detect and control.

The late Stephen Hawking, one of the most renowned theoretical physicists of our time, expressed concern about the potential risks of developing superintelligent AI. In a 2014 interview with the BBC, Hawking warned that "The development of full artificial intelligence could spell the end of the human race".[3] He went on to explain that once machines reach a point where they can improve themselves at a rapid pace, humans, with our slow

---

[3] Rory Cellan-Jones, "Stephen Hawking warns artificial intelligence could end mankind", *The BBC*, December 2, 2014.

biological evolution, would no longer be able to compete and we will be superseded as a result. Hawking reiterated his viewpoint during a Q&A session at the annual Zeitgeist Conference in 2016. He stated, "I believe there is no deep difference between what can be achieved by a biological brain and what can be achieved by a computer. It, therefore, follows that computers can, in theory, emulate human intelligence—and exceed it".[4]

Beyond a potential showdown with AI agents, a more immediate concern lies in how humans will harness superintelligent AI to wield power and influence. Similar to preceding technological advancements, humans will inevitably seek out ways to exploit superintelligent AI to achieve their objectives, whether that's delivering bias and misinformation over the Internet or exploiting it for cyberattacks, digital espionage, and deep surveillance. Equally, there is a looming danger of a strong central actor like OpenAI, Microsoft, or a state actor such as the Chinese Community Party monopolizing access to superintelligent systems and relevant hardware.

Seeing the problems posed by this scenario, initiatives such as StabilityAI advocate for an open-source and grassroots-driven approach to AI development. They warn against the path of centralized power and encourage the proliferation of distinct AI systems, each aligned with the values and perspectives of the communities they serve, mirroring the plurality and diversity of human values.

The Singularity

Building on the concept of superintelligent AI, the theory of *the Singularity* forecasts a future point of irrevocable societal change that will occur if and when AI surpasses human intelligence. This theory is based on the principle that a sufficiently advanced AI would be capable of designing an even more advanced version of itself, which could then design an even more advanced version, and so

---

[4] Stephen Hawking, "LCFI Launch: Stephen Hawking", *Leverhulme Centre for the Future of Intelligence*, Accessed July 10, 2023, http://lcfi.ac.uk/resources/cfi-launch-stephen-hawking.

forth, leading to a rapid and exponential increase in intelligence.

The term and theory were popularized by mathematician and science fiction author Vernor Vinge in his 1993 essay *The Coming Technological Singularity*. According to Vinge, the Singularity represents the end of the human era, as superintelligence would continue to upgrade itself, leading to an exponential increase in AI capabilities. This process would result in unfathomable changes to civilization, so much so that our current models of reality—the ways we think about and understand the world—would no longer be sufficient.

These ideas have been further explored and expanded upon by authors and thinkers like Ray Kurzweil. In his book *The Singularity is Near*, published in 2005, Kurzweil predicts that the Singularity will occur around the year 2045 and will lead to considerable societal and biological changes, as the line between humans and machines becomes increasingly blurred. Kurzweil suggests that humans will merge with AI, enhancing our intellectual, physical, and emotional capabilities.

Amid this possibility, it's important to revisit the existential risks of leading AI development in this direction. As previously noted, there are substantial concerns regarding the issue of aligning AI with human values and objectives. Experts argue that as AI systems become more intelligent and capable, the likelihood rises that they will deviate in ways unforeseen by us today. To counter this risk, Nick Bostrom emphasizes the need for substantial investments in research aimed at developing strategies to manage AI, ensuring that it contributes positively to humanity rather than causing harm.

One popular solution is to control and monitor the data used to train AI models. However, even with meticulous screening of data inputs to eliminate inappropriate content, ideologies, and knowledge, it's theoretically possible for superintelligent AI to uncover pathways to act contrary to human values or behave in unexpected ways. Using an inversion function, for example, the model could use its knowledge of positive behavior to acquire insights into the characteristics of negative behavior. If the model is trained to avert house fires, it could potentially learn how to start a house fire by adopting behavior contrary to the training data—all without ever being explicitly trained to engage in this behavior.

Similarly, training an AI to perform a specific task may inadvertently increase the likelihood of it doing the opposite of the intended behavior. This alignment problem has recently been termed *the Waluigi Effect*, inspired by the character Waluigi, the evil counterpart of Luigi in the Super Mario franchise. Humans, particularly teenagers, for instance, are inclined to do the opposite of what they are instructed and it's possible that developmental AI models could do the same.

Conversely, there are many experts who question whether it's possible for AI models to rebel or replicate and surpass human-level intelligence. One of these skeptics is the computer scientist Gordon Moore, co-founder of Intel and the originator of *Moore's Law* (the observation that the number of transistors on a microchip doubles approximately every two years). Moore has expressed doubts that the Singularity will occur within the predicted timeframe of the next 25 years or even at all. He argues that there are physical limitations to the computation speeds that machines can reach and that these limits will prevent the realization of the Singularity as envisioned by Vinge and Kurzweil.

Whether we are destined to reach the superintelligence phase of AI and witness the Singularity in our lifetimes remains uncertain, especially as it would require significant breakthroughs far beyond our current understanding and capabilities. In the meantime, contemplating the potential consequences of the Singularity is crucial for steering responsible AI development. For instance, if we create machines that match or surpass human intelligence, what are the implications? How do we ensure these AI systems align with human values and ethics?

According to the *precautionary principle*, a concept from risk management, it's valuable to address potential risks or harm even in the absence of scientific proof. The precautionary principle emphasizes the need for proactive action when there's the possibility of serious or irreversible harm to the environment or human health. In the context of superintelligence, this may involve the following measures.

1) Regulation and policy: Robust regulatory frameworks and policies are needed to address potential risks and provide guidelines for the responsible development and use of advanced AI systems. This involves setting safety and transparency standards, monitoring development, defining ethical boundaries for tech companies to operate under as well as potential intervention, if necessary.

Experts such as Daniel Colson, Executive director of the Artificial Intelligence Policy Institute, have proposed governments impose restrictions on AI firms, preventing them from acquiring vast supplies of hardware used to build super-advanced AI systems, while also making it illegal to build computing clusters above a certain processing threshold.[5] While these measures may appear severe, there is public support for government regulation and oversight of AI development. According to a 2023 poll organized by the Artificial Intelligence Policy Institute, 82% of American respondents said they don't trust tech executives to regulate AI, with 56% of respondents supporting a federal agency to regulate AI (compared to 14% who did not).[6] Similarly, a 2023 global study published by the University of Queensland and KPMG found that across 17 countries and 17,000 respondents, 71% of people surveyed were in favor of AI regulation[7], while the Ada Lovelace Institute and The Alan Turing Institute found that

---

[5] Daniel Colson, "One think tank vs. 'god-like' AI", *Politico*, August 15, 2023.

[6] Ryan Heath, "Exclusive poll: Americans distrust AI giants", *Axios.com,* August 9, 2023.

[7] N. Gillespie, S. Lockey, C. Curtis, J. Pool, J & A. Akbari, "Trust in Artificial Intelligence: A Global Study", *The University of Queensland and KPMG Australia*, 2023.

62% of 4,000 British respondents would like to see laws and regulations guiding the use of AI technologies.[8]

However, backing AI regulation doesn't automatically imply public confidence in the ability of governments to act effectively. As per the University of Queensland and KPMG study, confidence in the government's ability to regulate AI development stood at 49% in the U.S., 47% in Japan, 45% in the UK, 86% in China, 70% in India, and 60% in Singapore.

2) Global coordination: While country-level measures to regulate AI development are crucial, it's just as—or if not more—important to maintain alignment between countries and regions. Similar to the founding of the International Atomic Energy Agency to manage the safe use of nuclear power, OpenAI's co-founders have called for a global agency to rein in the development of superintelligence. This organization would be responsible for conducting assessments and audits of AI systems, designing and implementing safety standards, and defining ethical boundaries. While difficult to implement, agreements to restrict the pace of global AI development are another recommendation currently under discussion.

Existing forums for global cooperation, including the European Union, G7, and the United Nations are also in the process of designing processes to monitor and regulate the development of AI systems. However, as the COVID pandemic has shown us, achieving global cooperation is a challenging endeavor, especially in light of the present geopolitical environment and various schisms between Western powers, China, and Russia. If a country or several countries opt out of regulatory efforts or disregard global guidelines, the efficacy of participating nations' endeavors diminishes, resulting in a myriad of issues including inequitable access to AI hardware and technology, along with the migration of ambitious AI companies to non-participating states.

---

[8] "How do people feel about AI? A nationally representative survey of public attitudes to artificial intelligence in Britain", *Ada Lovelace Institute and The Alan Turing Institute*, 2023.

3) Public engagement: Next, to help more people identify and understand the potential risks and impacts of AI, it's crucial to encourage public participation in discussions and decision-making processes related to the development and deployment of advanced AI systems. This ensures that a wide range of perspectives and concerns are considered, while also encouraging ongoing debate over social, economic, ethical, and safety implications that could arise from developing superintelligent systems. Part of this debate may start as early as high school, with the Montana Digital Academy now offering courses covering AI history and ethics to high school students in the U.S. state of Montana, for example.

Other public initiatives include the United Nations AI for Good Global Summit, the Center for AI Safety's 2023 statement raising the risk of extinction from AI as a global priority, and the Future of Life Institute's open letter calling for AI companies to pause training AI models more powerful than GPT-4 for at least 6 months (which OpenAI has not signed). As a signee of the Future of Life Institute's open letter, Elon Musk has also launched a new company called xAI, with the mission of offering pragmatic alternatives to pausing the development of superintelligence.

With each new AI breakthrough, we can expect to see more non-government initiatives and public activities discussing the role and threat of AI, with the overall aim of ensuring that AI remains aligned with societal values and priorities.

Key Takeaways

1) Narrow AI, general AI, and superintelligent AI form the three potential stages of AI development. Narrow AI is designed for specific tasks, while general AI possesses broad cognitive capabilities similar to humans, and superintelligent AI surpasses human intelligence.

2) There are serious concerns regarding the control and alignment of superintelligent AI to ensure that it aligns with human goals and values.

3) It is difficult to discuss and imagine the future of AI without confronting the issue of the Singularity, which predicts a future point where the human race is overtaken and potentially overrun by AI agents.

4) It's important to discuss the potential implications of superintelligence and introduce early precautionary measures despite the absence of scientific proof.

Thought Exercises

1) What are your instincts regarding the possibility of the Singularity? Also, what alternative perspectives or potential developments are you currently overlooking?

2) What measures, if any, can humans take to prevent the Singularity from becoming a reality?

5

Machine Learning

No matter where your exploration of AI takes you, the path will invariably intersect with the field of machine learning. Whether it's forecasting stock prices, detecting fraudulent transactions, or powering speech recognition in virtual assistants, machine learning provides the core for many AI applications.

As a subfield of AI, the power of machine learning lies in its ability to learn from data and make predictions without being directly programmed. Given a set of inputs, the model will make a prediction about what it thinks will happen next based on the patterns learned from existing data. This might involve predicting the price of a house based on features such as its location, size, year built, and sales history.

This process of learning and understanding patterns in the data is known as *training*, whereby an algorithm is fed data, called a training set, and studies that data in order to learn patterns. If we take the example of a house price prediction model, the algorithm is shown many examples of houses along with their actual price value. The algorithm learns the relationship between the features of the houses, known as the explanatory variables, and their price valuation, known as the target variable. Once it's learned this relationship, it can predict the price of a new house based on its variables using what's called a *model* or *prediction model*. The model is a mathematical representation that maps all the explanatory variables to a target variable, such as the qualities of a house and its market value. The goal of training is to find the best model, which is the one that most accurately captures the relationship between the explanatory variables and the target variable.

It's crucial to realize that perfect alignment with the existing data is not necessarily the goal of designing a reliable model. This stems from a common pitfall in machine learning, known as *overfitting*. This occurs when a model is fine-tuned to the nuances and noise of the training data to such an extent that it captures insignificant and random fluctuations in the data.

While this results in exceptional performance when tested against the training dataset, it leads to a drastic decline in the model's ability to generalize new and unseen data. In its pursuit of achieving the best fit on the training data, the model fails to encapsulate the underlying relationships that are universally true beyond the training data. In essence, the model has memorized the training data rather than learning the true underlying patterns.

Thus, the objective of machine learning is to find a balance—one that fits the training data well enough to capture the true patterns and relationships without mirroring its exact patterns or noise in the data. Striking this balance between a model's capacity to learn from data and not overfitting or overlearning is one of the biggest challenges in machine learning and requires careful model design decisions, data handling, and evaluation methodologies.

In regard to model design, there are three overarching techniques that we will explore in this chapter, starting with supervised learning.

Supervised Learning

Supervised learning is a type of machine learning where the algorithm learns from a labeled dataset. Here, "labeled" means that the training data includes both the explanatory variables and the correct target variable. The house price prediction example is a case of supervised learning because the model is trained on a dataset of houses for which the explanatory variables (i.e., land size, year built, etc.) and the target variable (house price) are already known and included in the dataset.

Explanatory Variables				Target
Land Size (ft)	Year Built	Distance to City (miles)	No. of Rooms	House Price (USD)
5000	1990	10	4	300000
6000	2005	5	5	450000
7500	1985	15	3	280000
5500	2010	3	6	500000
4800	2000	8	4	400000
6200	1995	12	5	

Labeled

Unlabeled

Figure 4: Labeled vs. unlabeled data

As another example, consider the model for predicting the quickest route from point A to point B in Bangkok. First, you need a labeled dataset that includes numerous examples of routes from various points to various other points, along with information about how long each route took. The label in this case is the time it took for each route. The machine learning model, through training, would then learn to associate different factors such as distance, number of turns, speed limits, and other route characteristics with the time taken. Once trained, and given a new pair of start and end points, the model is able to predict the quickest route based on patterns learned from past examples.

In essence, supervised learning gives the model all the information it needs so that it can decipher relationships between the explanatory variables and a given target variable, such as house price or travel time. Please note that explanatory variables are also called the "independent variables" or "X" in machine learning literature, while the target variable is called the "dependent variable" or "y".

Unsupervised Learning

Unsupervised learning deals with unlabeled data. The model still has access to different explanatory variables but no corresponding target variable. In this case, you might have the same dataset describing house features, including land size and the number of rooms, but no information about the house price. As a consequence, it's impossible to predict the value of houses in this dataset without this missing variable. Unsupervised learning, therefore, looks at other ways of exploring the data.

In general, the goal of unsupervised learning is to find structure in the data, such as grouping similar variables together. Building on an earlier example, let's say you have access to the GPS data for thousands of taxi trips in Bangkok including travel times and addresses but no labels about popular pickup and drop-off points. Using unsupervised learning, you could use the data to explore and discover the structure within it. For example, you might identify clusters of trips that start or end in certain areas, effectively identifying popular pick-up and drop-off points. Likewise, you might discover recurring patterns in the data, such as specific routes that are frequently taken, essentially learning the main thoroughfares without ever being explicitly told what the main roads in Bangkok are.

This ability to discover unlabeled relationships means that unsupervised learning algorithms can be used in advance of supervised learning to prepare the data for prediction modeling. When used in this way, unsupervised algorithms help to clean up and label the data.

Reinforcement Learning

Used in various fields, including robotics, game playing, and navigation, reinforcement learning allows the model to learn by performing actions in a defined environment and receiving rewards or punishments based on its decisions. Opposite to unsupervised learning, reinforcement learning is told the target variable but needs to learn the values of the explanatory variables (which are unknown).

The learning process is guided by the goal of maximizing the total reward. To explain, let's consider a self-driving car that needs to navigate from point A to point B. The car has a map of the city and a GPS signal, but it needs to learn how to drive to the destination on its own. In reinforcement learning, the self-driving car would learn by trial and error.

It might start with random actions and receive a reward or penalty based on how well it performed. If it takes a shorter route, it might get a reward. If it violates traffic rules or takes a longer route, it might receive a penalty. Over time, by trying to maximize its total reward, the self-driving car would learn to effectively navigate the city.

Due to the exploratory nature of reinforcement learning, such models require significantly more time and computing power than other forms of machine learning to train.

Model Design

It's vital to remember that the model techniques discussed are not easily interchangeable. Each technique is tailored to solving a specific type of problem using a given dataset and their use cases tend not to overlap.

Supervised learning, for example, is generally the go-to approach when you have a lot of labeled data, in which you know both the explanatory variables and the target variable. For example, if you're developing an email spam filter and you have a dataset with emails that are already labeled as "spam" or "not spam" (target variable) and other information such as the name of the sender and the email title (explanatory variables), then supervised learning is an ideal technique for this task.

Unsupervised learning comes into play when you have plenty of input data but no corresponding target variable labels. The main goal is to uncover hidden patterns, clusters, or structures within the data. If you're tasked with customer segmentation as part of a marketing analytics project, unsupervised learning methods like clustering can help identify groups of similar customers based on their purchasing behaviors or preferences, for example. In its place, supervised learning would not be a suitable approach for discovering these unknown customer categories given there are no existing labels.

Reinforcement learning, meanwhile, is suitable for situations where a model learns to make decisions by interacting in an environment with a finite number of sequential decision actions. For instance, if you're designing a system for playing chess or a video game, reinforcement learning would be a prime candidate as it allows the AI to learn optimal strategies over time through trial and error. Reinforcement learning, though, cannot be used to predict house prices or categorize emails into spam or non-spam as these tasks don't involve sequential decision-making within a confined environment.

In summary, the choice between supervised, unsupervised, and reinforcement learning is not a matter of superiority or preference, but rather a matter of fit. It's about selecting the technique that best aligns with the data you have and the problem you are attempting to solve. Making the right choice can make the difference between a successful AI project and one that is destined to fail before you even start.

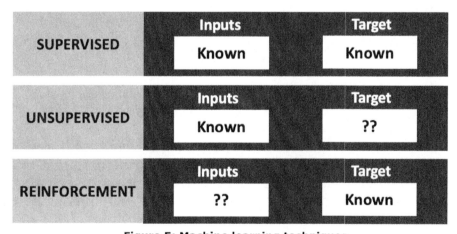

	Inputs	Target
SUPERVISED	**Known**	**Known**
UNSUPERVISED	**Known**	**??**
REINFORCEMENT	**??**	**Known**

Figure 5: Machine learning techniques

Practical Demonstration

To reinforce the difference between supervised, unsupervised, and reinforcement learning, let's explore three different model scenarios. To help with this practical demonstration, we will be using a hypothetical dataset, belonging to a fictional video game. In this video game, players control a character to collect items, avoid enemies, and maximize their score within a limited time period.

Variables:

PlayerID (unique identifier for each player)

Items_Collected (number of items the player's character collected)

Enemies_Avoided (number of enemies the player's character avoided)

Time_Taken (time in seconds taken to complete a mission)

Score (points earned by the player, based on items, enemies, and time taken)

PlayerID	Items_Collected	Enemies_Avoided	Time_Taken	Score
001	10	5	100	125
002	8	4	85	117
003	9	3	120	87
004	10	5	120	104
005	8	3	100	95
006	4	9	140	60
007	6	8	120	83

This dataset has five variables, also known as features or dimensions, and seven rows of values. Please note that this dataset is for illustrative purposes; in real-world scenarios, you would need a much larger dataset with many more rows in order to train a credible model.

Model 1: Supervised Learning

Objective: Predict the Score of a player given the other features

Explanatory variables: Items_Collected, Enemies_Avoided, Time_Taken

Target variable: Score

Steps

1) Divide the dataset into a training set (75%) and a test set (25%)
2) Choose an algorithm: In this case, a regression algorithm such as linear regression is a good choice because the target variable (Score) is a continuous variable.
3) Train the algorithm on the training data to build a model, which works by finding the correlation between different explanatory variables and the target variable.
4) Test the model on the test data to see how well it predicts the target variable (Score) using the remaining unused data.
5) Measure the accuracy using an evaluation metric such as Mean Squared Error (MSE), which is the average of the squares of the differences between the actual and predicted values.
6) Use the trained model to predict future data.

Model 2: Unsupervised Learning

Objective: Group players into clusters based on their playing style
Explanatory variables: Time_Taken, Score
Target variable: N/A (unknown)

Steps

1) Choose a clustering algorithm, such as *k*-means clustering.
2) Decide on the number of clusters/groups, i.e. $k = 3$.[9]
3) Train the algorithm on the explanatory variables. (There is no training-test data split in unsupervised learning.)

---

[9] As an explanatory technique, there are no fixed rules for determining the number of clusters to analyze. Note that if you set *k* to the same number of data points contained in the dataset, each data point automatically becomes a standalone cluster. Conversely, if you set *k* to 1, then all data points will be deemed as homogenous and fall inside one large cluster. You, therefore, want to avoid using a *k* value close to 1 or close to the maximum number of data points.

4) Analyze the clusters to see which players fall into which cluster and interpret the characteristics of each cluster. For example, we might find that the three clusters represent: aggressive players, balanced players, and defensive players.

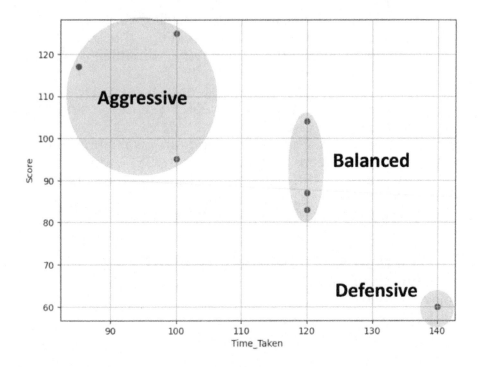

These three new categories can now be used to label each player in the dataset, providing a new variable/feature that we didn't know about previously.

PlayerID	Items_Collected	Enemies_Avoided	Time_Taken	Score	Type
001	10	5	100	125	Aggressive
002	8	4	85	117	Aggressive
003	9	3	120	87	Balanced
004	10	5	120	104	Balanced
005	8	3	100	95	Aggressive
006	4	9	140	60	Defensive
007	6	8	120	83	Balanced

Model 3: Reinforcement Learning

Objective: Develop an AI agent that can play the game and maximize the Score value.

Explanatory variables: Move left, move right, jump, crouch, advance forward

Target variable: Score

Steps

1) Define the state space: A combination of the player's position, items left, enemies nearby, etc.
2) Define the action space: Move left, move right, jump, crouch, advance forward.
3) Define the reward: For example, +50 for collecting an item, -50 for colliding with an enemy, and +100 for passing the mission.
4) Use an algorithm like Q-learning to train the agent. The agent will play the game multiple times. In the beginning, it will play randomly and make many mistakes.
5) Over time, the agent will learn the optimal strategy to play the game and maximize Score.

Other Approaches

In addition to the three approaches to machine learning that we have discussed, there are two other variants that lie between supervised and unsupervised learning, called *semi-supervised learning* and *self-supervised learning* respectively.

In the case of semi-supervised learning, there is typically a large amount of data but only some of it is actually labeled. The idea is to use the labeled data to train an initial model and make predictions on the unlabeled data. The most confident predictions are then used to label the unlabeled data and expand the labeled training set. The prediction model can then be retrained on the combination of the originally labeled and the self-labeled data. In this way, semi-supervised learning seeks to benefit from the additional (albeit imperfectly labeled) data. For instance, you might have GPS data for millions of taxi rides but only have the route times for a few thousand of those rides. Using the known route times to train an initial model, you can then use that model to predict the route times for rides missing that variable based on their start point, end point, and other variables such as the day of the week.

In the case of self-supervised learning, all data is considered unlabeled, but the structure within the data is used to provide supervision. In other words, the training labels are automatically generated from the input data itself, without human annotation. This is done by creating a learning task where the objective is to predict some part of the input data. For example, a self-supervised learning algorithm may learn to predict the next word in a sentence or the next frame in a video. The goal is to design a task where the correct answer is available, allowing the model to learn from the data directly.

A real-world example of self-supervised learning is the masked language model training objective used in transformer-based language models such as Google's BERT (Bidirectional Encoder Representations from Transformers). During training, some portion of the input data such as a word in a sentence is masked, and the model is trained to predict the masked word based on the rest of the sentence. This allows the model to learn useful features about language from the data itself, without requiring explicit labels for each example.

Another common example comes from the field of computer vision, where a portion of an image might be obscured and the model is tasked with predicting the missing part. In this case, the model takes an image and purposedly obscures a part of it, like covering a portion of the image with a black box. The model then predicts what's hidden behind the black box by analyzing the surrounding context and making an educated guess. For instance, if the covered area is around a person's face, the model might predict that it's likely a face. As the model is exposed to more images, it learns to predict more hidden parts. Through this process, the model becomes better at recognizing objects, patterns, and relationships without explicit labels for every image.

In summary, semi-supervised learning is used when you have some labeled data and lots of unlabeled data, while self-supervised learning can be used on data without preexisting labels to predict hidden features.

Key Takeaways

1) Machine learning allows systems to learn from data and make predictions without explicit programming.

3) Training involves feeding a machine learning algorithm a dataset to learn patterns and relationships. The goal is to find a model that accurately captures the underlying patterns without overfitting the training data.

3) There are three primary types of machine learning models:

- Supervised learning uses labeled data with known explanatory variables and a known target variable to train the model.

- Unsupervised learning deals with known explanatory variables and aims to discover hidden patterns and structures within the data to create a new target variable.

- Reinforcement learning involves learning through trial and error in an environment with rewards and punishments in order to achieve a predefined target.

4) Model selection depends on the type of data you have available and the problem you are attempting to solve.

Thought Exercises

1) What is a use case for supervised learning? (Hint: think of a website that makes a prediction based on past data)

2) What is a use case for unsupervised learning? (Hint: think of a model for sorting items)

3) What is a use case for reinforcement learning? (Hint: think of a game or closed environment with a limited number of potential actions)

****

If you are enjoying the content of this book so far, please consider sharing your thoughts with a review on Amazon or contact the author directly at oliver.theobald@scatterplotpress.com.

6

Deep Learning

From self-driving cars to large language models, the ability of deep learning to learn from raw data and process large datasets has dramatically broadened the use cases for artificial intelligence. However, like all technologies, deep learning has its own unique limitations and challenges that we will examine in this chapter.

Before we dive in, it's important to explain the connection between deep learning and machine learning. Machine learning, as discussed, involves algorithms and models that improve with experience and exposure to data. As a subfield of machine learning, deep learning takes the foundational principles of machine learning and applies its own techniques to even larger and more complex datasets. This involves the use of artificial neural networks with deep and multiple layers stacked together to form a model.

While artificial neural networks are not a direct replica of the human brain, (with the human brain estimated to contain 100 billion neurons, outnumbering the number of stars in the galaxy, and more than one thousand kilometers of interconnections), they are loosely inspired by it. Artificial neural networks consist of interconnected nodes or neurons that process and pass on information to the next layer of neurons—similar to how neurons in the brain process and transmit information. The first layer of neurons in the network, for example, might recognize basic features in images, such as edges. The next layer might put these edges together to recognize shapes, the layer after that might recognize fur patterns, and so on, until the final layer recognizes the overall image as a cat.

Like machine learning, deep learning makes use of supervised, unsupervised, and reinforcement learning techniques. In the case of supervised learning, a neural network, such as a convolutional neural network, can be trained to recognize images by studying a large number of labeled images (with the labels describing the image) and learning to identify the labeled objects contained in those images.

In the case of unsupervised learning, deep learning is often used to simplify and reduce the dimensionality (number of features) in the data or remove noise from it.

In reinforcement deep learning, neural networks are combined with reinforcement learning techniques to create systems that can learn to make a sequence of decisions. An example is the AlphaGo program developed by DeepMind, which learned to play the game of Go at a superhuman level by studying past games played by humans as well as games played against itself.

Deep Learning Models

There are various types of neural networks employed in deep learning, each with its own unique strengths and common use cases. In this section, we will examine convolutional and recurrent neural networks as well as transformer networks, which play a major role in NLP and computer vision (discussed in Chapter 7 and Chapter 10 respectively).

Convolutional Neural Networks

CNNs represent a major advancement in the field of computer vision, enabling machines to see and interpret visual data. From facial recognition to self-driving cars, CNNs are integral to computer vision and other AI applications. In fact, the name "convolutional" comes from the mathematical operation by the same name, which is a specialized type of linear operation often utilized for image processing.

CNNs excel at identifying spatial hierarchies or patterns in images by processing small chunks of the image, allowing them to recognize complex shapes and structures. Prior to CNNs, image data was typically fed into neural networks as one-dimensional arrays[10]. This, however, reduced the spatial information contained in the image. To elaborate, images are typically recorded as two-dimensional structures, consisting of rows and columns of pixels. Each pixel represents a value that represents the color or intensity at that specific location in the image. To process an image using a traditional neural network, the image is transformed into a one-dimensional array, also known as a vector. This transformation involves concatenating (meaning "joining") the rows or columns of the image into a long linear sequence of values.

As an example, let's say we have a grayscale image of dimensions 64x64 pixels. Each pixel in the image represents a grayscale intensity ranging from 0 to 255. By flattening this image into a one-dimensional array, we obtain a sequence of 4,096 values, where each value represents the intensity of a pixel. By representing the image as a one-dimensional array, we can feed it into a neural network as input, which then processes that array and performs computations on the values of each element.

While flattening the image into a one-dimensional array simplifies the representation of the image, it also eliminates the spatial structure and relationships between neighboring pixels. This loss of spatial information can limit the ability of the neural network to capture complex patterns and spatial dependencies within images. Recognizing a face, for instance, is not just about identifying individual facial features like the eyes, nose, or mouth, but also understanding their relative positions to each other. Traditional neural networks, though, fail to effectively account for such spatial hierarchy between features.

---

[10] A one-dimensional array, also known as a vector, is a data structure to store elements in a linear sequence with the elements arranged in a single row or column.

To overcome this limitation, CNNs preserve the spatial structure of images by operating directly on the two-dimensional or three-dimensional representations of images, allowing them to capture local patterns, spatial hierarchy, and spatial relationships between features. Unlike traditional neural networks, CNNs maintain the spatial relationships between pixels by learning image features using small squares of input data. This method is less sensitive to object position and distortion within the image, enabling the model to recognize an object even if its appearance varies in some way. For example, when a CNN is trained to recognize a turtle, it learns to detect its distinct features like the shape of the shell, the presence of flippers, and the general body structure. These collections of features are consistently present across different images of turtles, irrespective of their overall positions or poses. By capturing the spatial relationships among these features, the CNN can effectively generalize and recognize turtles, regardless of whether they are crawling, standing, or partially hidden inside their shell.

In terms of their design, CNNs consist of a series of layers that filter the raw pixel data of an image to extract and learn higher-level features, which the model can then use for classification. Higher-level features refer to visual elements that are built upon simpler features detected in earlier layers, such as edges, lines, and textures. In other words, the earlier layers capture basic visual elements that are present in the input images and as the information flows through subsequent layers of the network, higher-level features are learned by combining and abstracting these low-level features.

Another important aspect of CNNs is the pooling layers that follow the convolutional layers. When passing an image through a CNN, it goes through several layers that detect different features like edges, shapes, and objects. As mentioned, these features are combined to understand what's present in the image. However, the information can be quite detailed, which can make the network overly complex and slow to run. Pooling layers solve this problem by reducing the dimensionality of the data. This involves summarizing and preserving the most relevant information, which results in a more manageable and efficient representation. By compressing the information, pooling therefore decreases the size of the data and the number of calculations needed, speeding up the overall network. Pooling layers also make the network more robust by focusing on important features rather than their exact position. This enables the network to recognize objects even if they appear slightly shifted or in different parts of the image.

Recurrent Neural Networks

Renowned for their inherent ability to remember, RNNs have been central to groundbreaking developments in various fields including natural language processing, speech recognition, and time series prediction.

Popularized by John Hopfield in the early 1980s, RNNs were originally designed to overcome the limitations of existing artificial neural networks. Notably, traditional feed-forward neural networks, including CNNs, are not designed to deal with sequential inputs. (A feedforward neural network is an artificial neural network where connections between the decision nodes do not form a loop or cycle).

For tasks such as language translation, speech recognition, or time-series prediction, the order of the inputs often carries crucial information, and the ability to handle sequences is a key requirement. While traditional neural networks assume that all inputs (and outputs) are independent of each other, RNNs leverage the sequential nature of their input data. By processing inputs in sequence and having a form of memory, they can account for the context provided by preceding elements. This allows them to excel at tasks where the sequence and context matter, such as sentences or time series data. They achieve this by creating loops that pass information from one step in the sequence to the next, effectively giving the network a basic form of memory. In practice, each neuron or unit in an RNN has a "hidden state" which acts as a point of memory. This hidden state is a function of the current input and the previous hidden state, allowing the network to retain information from prior inputs in the sequence.

To better understand this concept, let's consider the task of predicting the next word in a sentence as an example. A feed-forward network might be given a fixed number of previous words and be trained to predict the next, but it would treat these input words independently, ignoring the order in which they appear. An RNN, on the other hand, would process the sentence word by word, retaining information from previous words as it goes along, thereby capturing the sequence's context.

RNNs, however, possess limitations and chief among these is the *vanishing gradient problem*. The vanishing gradient problem occurs when a deep neural network struggles to learn and make meaningful updates to its weights during training. This happens because the gradients (slopes) of the loss function for the network's weights become extremely small as they are passed backward through the layers (backpropagation). These gradients are calculated by multiplying the gradients from the subsequent layers with the weights connecting the current layer. As the network becomes deeper, this multiplication can lead to a situation where the gradients diminish significantly as they propagate backward through multiple layers. This can result in very small gradient values, leading to slow weight updates or adjustments. As a result, the network makes only tiny adjustments to its weights and it either takes a very long time to complete or the network fails to learn complex patterns in the data.

To gain a clearer grasp of this concept, it helps to think of the neural network as a hiker trying to find the best path to reach their destination. The hiker adjusts its path (which is the weights) by looking at how much the slope (which is the gradient) changes. If the slope is steep, it means there's a lot to learn, so the hiker makes bigger adjustments to its path. If the slope is gentle, it means there's not much to learn, so the hiker only makes small changes to its path. In some cases, especially with deep networks or long sequences like in RNNs, the slopes can become very flat. When this happens, the hiker gets stuck because it can't make meaningful adjustments to its path (which is the weights). Thus, much like a hiker struggling on a flat mountain path, the network might take forever to learn or become disorientated in the process.

As a practical example, imagine that you are training a neural network to identify various types of animals in images. When the network faces tricky examples such as a zebra, the gradient is already extremely tiny, which reflects how much the model should fine-tune its internal settings to improve its recognition. As a result, the network learns at a sluggish pace or it may even become stuck and fail to accurately recognize animal images that are difficult to classify.

In the context of RNNs, the vanishing gradient problem makes it difficult for the model to learn long-range dependencies in the data (discussed also in Chapter 7) because it struggles to learn relationships between inputs that are distanced apart. For instance, in a language processing task, an RNN might find it challenging to connect information from the beginning of a long sentence with relevant words or phrases at the end of the sentence. This happens because the RNN's ability to remember and use information from earlier inputs gets weaker with more added inputs.

This problem has led to the development of more advanced types of RNNs like long short-term memory (LSTM) and gated recurrent unit (GRU), which introduce gates to control the flow of information. Acting as a switch, a gate is a mechanism that controls the flow of information within the network. It determines how much information should be passed through and how much information should be blocked or forgotten at each step. This allows the model to selectively retain important information, helping to mitigate the vanishing gradient problem. This architecture has proven extremely effective, enabling RNNs to tackle complex and nuanced tasks in NLP, including machine translation, sentiment analysis, text summarization, and language generation.

Transformer Networks

Transformer networks represent a significant leap forward in dealing with sequential data and especially in natural language processing. By focusing on the parts of the data that matter most and processing sequences more efficiently, they have opened a new paradigm in deep learning.

Transformer networks were formally introduced in a 2017 paper published by Google titled *Attention is All You Need*. They were designed primarily to address the shortcomings of existing models in handling sequential data, especially in the field of NLP. Prior to the introduction of transformers, recurrent neural networks and their variants such as long short-term memory and gated recurrent unit were the dominant models for sequential data tasks. While these models performed well, they processed sequences in a linear manner, considering one element at a time. This approach resulted in two unique problems: computational inefficiency and difficulty in capturing long-distance dependencies in the data.

First, sequential processing made it challenging and slow to effectively parallelize computations during training. Second, even though LSTMs and GRUs were designed to mitigate the vanishing gradient problem of standard RNNs and better capture long-range dependencies, they still struggled with very long sequences.

Transformer networks were thus developed to tackle these two issues. They introduced a mechanism called *attention*, which allows the model to weigh the relevance of different elements in the input sequence when producing an output, thus enabling it to focus more on important parts and less on others.

This mechanism is useful in NLP, where the meaning of a word can depend heavily on its context in a sentence or document. For instance, consider the following English sentence: "I took the dog that bit me to the vet". In this sentence, the word bit" is closely related to "dog" and me", while "vet" is more relevant to "I" and "took". A transformer model uses attention mechanisms to determine these dependencies. It assigns higher weights to "dog" and "me" when processing "bit" and higher weights to "I" and "took" when processing "vet". Moreover, if we were translating this sentence into a language like German, where the verb often comes at the end of the sentence, the transformer's attention mechanism would allow it to associate the verb in English with the corresponding verb in German, even though they are in different positions within their respective sentences.

Importantly, transformer models can compute the attention weights for all elements of the sequence in parallel, leading to significant improvements in computational efficiency. Moreover, by directly attending to all other words in the sequence, regardless of their position, transformer models capture both short-term and long-term dependencies contained within the data.

This architecture has proven extremely effective at natural language processing tasks with the ability to process entire sentences or even paragraphs at once— instead of sequentially. Specifically, they make use of the attention mechanism to weigh the importance of different words in understanding the context of a sentence. This has resulted in state-of-the-art models like GPT (generative pretrained transformer) by OpenAI and BERT by Google. These models, pre-trained on a large database of text and fine-tuned for specific tasks, have significantly advanced the field, demonstrating human-level performance on a range of different benchmarks.

Challenges

In general, building and training any type of deep learning network, especially reinforcement learning-based models, requires substantial computation and processing resources. This includes processing massive amounts of data and performing complex calculations that necessitate considerable memory and powerful graphical processing units. However, recent technological advancements and cloud-based solutions have made these resources more affordable and accessible, enabling more parties to participate in deep learning.

Next, deep learning models thrive on data and while the recent explosion of big data has provided important fuel for these data-hungry models, the quality of data is important too. Erroneous or biased data can cause misleading results or reinforce existing biases. In addition, deep learning models contain a tendency to model intricate patterns in the training data, which can be a strength as well as a potential weakness. There's a risk that models might overfit the training data, learning noise and specific details that don't generalize well to unseen data.

However, perhaps the biggest challenge within the field of deep learning is the black box nature of these prediction models. In general, it's difficult to understand why a particular prediction was made and this is problematic in scenarios like healthcare or judiciary scenarios where transparency and trust are crucial. As discussed in Chapter 3, efforts are ongoing in the field of explainable AI to make models more transparent and interpretable.

Understanding these strengths and weaknesses is critical when deciding on potential uses for deep learning. Businesses without access to massive troves of data and GPU resources, for instance, may not be suitable candidates for deep learning, especially if they need a model that is transparent and easy to visualize.

Key Takeaways

1) Deep learning is an advanced subfield of machine learning that uses artificial neural networks with deep and multiple layers to learn and model complex patterns in data.

2) Deep learning models include convolutional neural networks (CNNs), recurrent neural networks (RNNs), and transformer networks. Each has its own strengths and common use cases.

3) Due to the complexity of the neural networks and the large amount of data they handle, deep learning models require substantial computational resources. Deep learning

models can also suffer from limitations such as the black box nature of their decision-making mechanisms and the risk of overfitting patterns in the training data.

7

Natural Language Processing

Beyond numerical data, a vast amount of human knowledge and experience is captured in text and audio. The ubiquity of words in daily life and the need for effective human-computer interactions make the ability to process human language a crucial part of artificial intelligence.

As a multidisciplinary field straddling linguistics, computer science, and AI, natural language processing empowers computers with the capability to understand and reproduce human language. Inspired by linguistics—the study of language and semantics—NLP was originally designed for parsing text in databases using coding rule systems, but over time, it merged with common algorithms from machine learning to evolve into a novel and specialized field of computational linguistics. Now, as a field of its own, NLP involves analyzing human language with reduced emphasis on quantitative problem-solving, which is typically the focus of other subfields related to AI.

Early Development

To grasp the impact of recent developments in NLP, it's important to see what's changed and where it all began. Originally, NLP consisted of human-programmed rule-based systems, where linguistic experts would manually encode rules of language into a computer program. While some of these earlier approaches obtained minor success in domain-specific cases, they were inherently limited by the complexity and variability of human language. One example is ELIZA, which was one of the first chatbots developed by Joseph Weizenbaum at MIT in the 1960s.

This included a version of ELIZA designed to emulate a psychotherapist using its ability to reflect user statements back in the form of a question, as demonstrated in the following example.

Example

Input: I am feeling sad.

Output: I see, can you tell me more about why you are feeling sad?

If a user said, "I am feeling sad", ELIZA might respond by replying, "I see, can you tell me more about why you are feeling sad?" While the output was impressive at the time, the ELIZA chatbox was simply following predefined rules and presenting itself as more intelligent than it actually was—especially as it didn't understand the full context of the conversation.

During the late 1980s and 1990s, the landscape of NLP research evolved with the introduction of machine learning methods. Rather than relying on hard-coded rules, new methods used statistical-based models to learn patterns from large amounts of labeled data. This development significantly improved overall performance and broadened the scope of tasks that NLP researchers could tackle. Despite several advancements, these methods still had limitations. Notably, they relied on carefully engineered features derived from expert knowledge, which was labor-intensive and unable to fully capture the richness and subtlety of human language. In addition, these methods struggled to capture longer-range dependencies within a text, which refers to the relationship between words or elements in a sentence that are not adjacent or close together but that still influence each other's meaning. To explain why, let's consider the following example.

Example

Input: The girl, who was wearing a red hat that her mother bought her for her birthday last year, ran down the street.

Here, the main subject ("The girl") and the main action ("ran down the street") are separated by a long clause ("who was wearing a red hat that her mother bought her for her birthday last year"). Despite this distance, we understand that it is the girl who is running, not the mother or the hat. Traditional NLP methods, however, struggled to capture and understand this long-range dependency.

Next, traditional NLP methods lacked the ability to leverage the benefits of distributed representations, a method of symbolizing words as vectors in high-dimensional space. This approach, commonly known as *word embeddings*, enables semantically similar words to exist closer together, thereby enriching the understanding of textual data.

To understand this approach, it helps to think of a high-dimensional space as a coordinate system where each word has its own position. Words with similar meanings or usage, such as "cat" and "dog", tend to be closer to each other because they share a similar semantic meaning related to animals. Similarly, words like "AI" and "artificial intelligence" would be close together because they share the same meaning. These close relationships in a high-dimensional space are called vectors or word embeddings, which resemble an ordered list of numerical values. Using these word embeddings, NLP models are capable of understanding relationships between words and capturing their contextual meaning. This allows the model to see similarities and differences between words and make more accurate predictions or enhance their understanding.

As mentioned, traditional NLP methods struggled to analyze vectors in a high-dimensional space. This limitation and the need to overcome it drove the adoption of newer, more sophisticated deep learning architectures such as recurrent neural networks and transformer networks. Designed to examine the full context and multiple sentences at a time, these techniques exhibited a superior ability to handle longer-range dependencies in text, marking a significant advancement in the field of NLP.

Transformer networks are now used heavily in NLP models including OpenAI's GPT model and Google's BERT model. In recent years, NLP has also benefited from several other emerging trends including zero-shot learning, where models learn to generalize using fewer labeled examples. This is especially useful when labeled data is scarce, which is often the case for less common and low-resource languages.

In practice, rather than relying solely on labeled examples, zero-shot learning leverages auxiliary information or semantic relationships to make predictions on new, unfamiliar classes. In other words, rather than training the model on numerous examples for every class, the model is trained on a smaller selection of classes. Then, when presented with a completely new class that it hasn't seen before, the model uses the hints and relationships it learned from the initial training data to make a prediction.

In effect, this allows the model to generalize and perform tasks in domains it wasn't explicitly trained to do. As an example, imagine you have a model that has learned to identify different animal classes, but the model has never seen a zebra before. If the model knows that zebras are similar to horses but they have black and white stripes, the model can recognize a zebra without ever seeing any direct examples of a zebra. In this case, the class "zebra" is already labeled in the dataset as a horse with black and white stripes.

Another promising trend has been self-supervised learning, which has been one of the driving forces behind the success of large language models such as GPT-3. This approach describes models that learn representations from unlabeled data, leveraging the abundant unannotated text available on the Internet.

In the context of GPT-3 and large language models, learning involves two main steps: pretraining and fine-tuning. In the pretraining phase, the model is exposed to a large collection of text, sourced from books, articles, web pages, and other sources. Here, the model learns to predict the next word in a sentence based on the preceding context, such as the following example.

Example
Input: "The cat sat on the _____"

In this example, the model needs to predict the next word after "the", which might be a word like "mat". The process repeats for numerous sentences in the dataset, exposing the model to a wide range of words and contexts. Through self-learning, the model learns to capture the statistical patterns and relationships contained in the text. It learns that after "The cat sat on the", words like "mat", "chair", or "floor" are likely to follow based on patterns observed from the training data.

By continuously training on a diverse range of sentences, the model gradually develops a strong understanding of language. It learns to recognize grammatical structures, understand the meaning of different words, and grasp the contextual relationships between words. This pretraining phase helps the model acquire a broad knowledge of language, allowing it to generate coherent and contextually relevant responses in conversations.

After pretraining, the model enters the fine-tuning phase. During this phase, the model is trained on specific supervised tasks with labeled data. For example, it can be fine-tuned on a conversational dataset where inputs and corresponding responses are provided. By training on this labeled data, the model learns to generate appropriate responses based on different inputs.

NLU & NLG

Broadly speaking, NLP can be divided into two distinct approaches: natural language understanding (NLU) and natural language generation (NLG). NLU enables a model to comprehend and derive meaning from human language, while NLG empowers a model to generate coherent and contextually appropriate text. This involves creating entire sentences, paragraphs, or even entire articles. NLG can be used for tasks such as generating descriptions of data, writing news stories, summarizing text, or creating conversational agents (known as chatbots). The core process involves determining what information to include and how to organize it (document planning), before putting the information into appropriate sentences (sentence planning), and then realizing the sentence plans in the actual text (text realization).

NLU, meanwhile, aims to extract meaning, sentiment, intent, and other semantic features from the text to perform sentiment analysis, named entity recognition, or text classification.

In terms of their application, both approaches start with raw, unstructured text data. This data emanates from various sources such as databases, APIs, scraped website content, user inputs, and chat logs. As with any data processing data, the raw data is cleaned, which usually involves removing inconsistencies, inaccuracies, or irrelevant information. Depending on the source of the data, this could involve tasks such as reformatting and removing or correcting typos.

Using a variety of techniques and preprocessing algorithms, the text is converted into a structured format that machines can process and understand. This involves tasks such as tokenization (breaking text into individual words or tokens), stemming (reducing words to their root form, i.e., "naturally" > "nature"), and removing stop words (common words such as "and", "the", and "a" that don't provide informational value) as well as unnecessary white spaces.

Natural Language Understanding

After transforming the text into a suitable format, various tasks can take place. In the case of natural language understanding, common tasks include topic modeling, sentiment analysis, named entity recognition, and text classification. Sentiment analysis involves determining the sentiment or emotion of a sentence or document, usually categorized as positive, negative, or neutral. Named entity recognition identifies and classifies named entities (i.e., persons, organizations, locations) in a text. Text classification classifies text into predefined categories, such as spam detection in emails and categorizing news articles. Lastly, as an unsupervised learning approach, topic modeling is used to discover abstract topics within a text document.

After undertaking one or more of these tasks, the model is evaluated based on appropriate metrics (such as accuracy, precision, recall, F1-score) to measure its performance. Then, once the model is evaluated and fine-tuned, it is deployed to real-world applications and used to inform decisions. Common examples include chatbots and virtual assistants such as Apple's Siri, Google Assistant, and Amazon's Alexa. These applications employ NLP to understand user commands and generate appropriate responses, enabling users to set reminders, search the Internet, control home devices, and so forth. In the realm of social media, NLU is used for sentiment analysis, helping businesses understand public sentiment towards their brand by analyzing text data from social media posts or customer reviews. The same technology can also aid in detecting online harassment or toxic behavior on online platforms.

Natural Language Generation

Having discussed common tasks in natural language understanding, let's revisit natural language generation. Following the data preprocessing stage, NLG typically consists of three stages: document planning, sentence planning, and text realization.

Document planning is the initial stage where the content to be included in the output text is decided. The system identifies the information from the source data that needs to be conveyed in the text. For instance, if an NLG model is generating a weather report, the document planning stage will identify the key data points to be included in the report, such as temperature, precipitation, and humidity. This stage includes organizing the selected content into a coherent structure and determining the order and manner in which the information will be presented.

Sentence planning, known too as *microplanning*, next determines how to express the selected information in linguistic terms. It decides on the specific words and phrases that can be used to represent the information. It also determines the structure of the sentences, taking into account different aspects such as grammatical correctness, cohesion with the surrounding sentences, and variability in expressions to avoid repetitiveness. Using the weather report example, this stage would involve choosing whether to say "It's expected to be sunny" or "Sunshine is predicted", among other considerations.

Lastly, text realization is where the actual text is generated. Here, the system transforms the linguistic representations from the previous stage into a final, fluent text. It ensures proper grammatical structures and pays attention to other aspects of the language such as punctuation and agreement between subjects and verbs. Using the weather report example again, this last step would involve generating the final form such as "Tomorrow, it's expected to be sunny with a high of 25 degrees".

These three stages often involve complex algorithms and rules, and more recently, newer language models such as GPT have proved highly successful at generating fluent and coherent text, leading to significant advances in the field of NLG and generative AI, which we'll discuss further in the following chapter.

Challenges

As with other areas of artificial intelligence, NLP is not without potential challenges and headaches! First, understanding the intricate nuances of human language, including irony, sarcasm, and cultural references poses a major challenge in the field of NLP.

Second, subtle changes in the text or context can shift the meaning of a word or phrase, and while this is easy for humans to perceive, it is notably difficult for machines to notice and comprehend. One example is the interpretation of homographs, which are words spelled the same but possess more than one meaning. The word "bass", for example, can mean a type of fish or a low, deep voice or musical instrument depending on the context. Similarly, the phrase "It's raining cats and dogs" doesn't literally mean animals are falling from the sky. Deciphering the meaning of such phrases is something that comes naturally to humans but is difficult for NLP models.

Issues such as language bias, model interpretability, data privacy, and the lack of high-quality annotated data for low-resource languages are other areas of concern and ongoing development. The issue of bias in NLP is a particularly thorny issue. This is because AI models tend to learn and replicate the biases contained in the training data, leading to biased predictions. This is problematic when NLP models are used in sensitive areas like recruitment or loan approval, where biased outcomes can have significant impacts on people's lives.

Ethical considerations, particularly around privacy, are also crucial. Text data, whether from social media, emails, or other sources, often contains sensitive or personal information. Hence, handling this data responsibly, adhering to data privacy regulations, and anonymizing data to protect individual identities become paramount responsibilities for those involved with collecting the training data and building the model.

Lastly, the development of NLP models for low-resource languages and multilingual contexts presents challenges. While a lot of work in NLP has been done in English, there's a scarcity of high-quality labeled data for many other languages. This lack of resources makes it challenging to develop robust NLP models that can understand and generate text in other languages. Furthermore, creating models that can handle text in multiple languages simultaneously also represents an ongoing challenge in terms of model sophistication and training.

Key Takeaways

1) Natural language processing is a multidisciplinary field that empowers computers to process, understand, and generate human language.

2) NLP can be divided into natural language understanding and natural language generation. NLU concentrates on extracting meaning, sentiment, and other semantic features from the text, while NLG focuses on generating coherent and contextually appropriate text.

3) Challenges in NLP include understanding the intricacies of human language, such as irony and cultural references, language subtlety, addressing bias, ensuring model interpretability, protecting data privacy, and developing NLP models for low-resource languages.

8

Generative AI

In the ever-evolving world of AI, a unique variant of machine intelligence is rapidly breaking into software applications and mainstream use. In this chapter, we will explore generative AI, looking at how it differs from its traditional counterpart, and discuss how its rich creativity is changing the landscape of content creation, with a particular focus on generative adversarial networks and the battle for available training data.

First, to understand the strengths of generative AI, it's important to understand how it differs from traditional AI. The first distinction between generative AI and traditional AI is found in their outputs. Traditional AI, which is sometimes referred to as *discriminative AI*, is trained to discriminate, classify, or predict based on input data fed into a model. This approach powers a variety of AI applications including recommendation systems and search engines. Generative AI, on the other hand, learns the underlying patterns of input data but rather than provide a prediction or insight, it uses that learned knowledge to generate an output that is similar but different from the training data.

ChatGPT, developed by OpenAI, is a prominent example of generative AI. Instead of predicting a likely output to a given input, ChatGPT is designed to generate coherent and contextually appropriate responses, whether that be drafting emails, writing essays, creating poetry, or simulating human dialogue.

Similarly, new software applications such as DALL-E (also developed by OpenAI), Midjourney, and Stable

Diffusion are making waves in the domain of art and image creation.

Visual outputs can be generated using what's called a generative adversarial network (GAN), a type of generative AI model that consists of two neural networks: a generator and a discriminator. During training, the generator and discriminator are pitted against each other in a competitive environment. The generator aims to produce realistic outputs that can fool the discriminator, while the discriminator aims to correctly identify whether the outputs are real or generated. In practice, the generator learns the target art style by observing and analyzing a vast dataset of existing artworks. Acting as a type of art critic, the discriminator then evaluates these generated images and issues feedback on their authenticity. Initially, the discriminator can easily identify the generated images as computer-generated due to the lack of resemblance to the training data. Using feedback from the discriminator, the generator adjusts its approach and through multiple feedback loops, the generator improves its ability to produce convincing artwork.

Throughout this entire process, the generator and discriminator are engaged in a competition against each other. The generator aims to produce art that the discriminator cannot distinguish from real artwork, while the discriminator seeks to improve its ability to differentiate between real and fake art. This adversarial competition drives both sides to evolve and learn from each other. Over time, the competition and ongoing feedback loop lead to a point of convergence where the generator becomes so proficient at creating art (resembling the style of the training data) that it deceives the discriminator.

Building on their success in the domain of image generation, researchers are also developing GANs for generating audio, music, writing, and even three-dimensional objects, leading to a further explosion in AI-generated content.

Data as a New Asset Class

Riding the wave of large language models powered by OpenAI's GPT architecture and advances in GAN techniques, generative AI is set to radically transform the physics of content creation and creative expression. From producing full-length films to customer service avatars trained on customer service logs and product documentation, as well as simulating realistic video game and esports environments, the possibilities are suddenly closer than many people expected.

Underpinning these developments is access to relevant training data and the growing adoption of generative AI software tools is set to unlock a new dimension of value for existing data. In sports, for example, match data and video footage of professional athletes can be monetized to create new and unique content. While this data has traditionally been used for entertainment and post-match analysis (as popularized in the film and novel *Moneyball*), it can now be commercialized for creative use cases as well.

One example comes from Behaviol, a digital sports company, working on a platform where gamers can acquire and develop AI sports stars to compete in virtual tournaments. The company is starting with cricket, after purchasing five years of player data to train and generate unique AI player avatars. This development marks a departure from traditional sports games, where in-game athletes come with preprogrammed actions and fixed behaviors.

Generative AI will be used by Behaviol to study the movements, techniques, and playing styles of real athletes by training AI on their match data and video footage. By doing so, Behaviol can recreate the actions, style, and performance of athletes in a virtual environment. This will enable gamers to play alongside AI-generated athletes and make it possible to simulate hypothetical scenarios, such as pitting Michael Jordan against modern basketball stars.

This new path of game and content creation opens up fertile space for athletes, broadcasters, and sporting franchises to commercialize their data in innovative ways and transform the market valuation of different data classes, including player data and video footage.

In a similar vein, actors, producers, directors, and film/television companies may also be enticed to commercialize their archives, including scripts, dialogue, scenes, and visual elements to produce AI-generated films and TV series. Actors and other industry professionals, though, are concerned about the potential for AI to create digital doppelgängers that replace human talent, especially for scriptwriters, new talent, and actors playing non-starring roles. Training AI models on an actor's film archive, for example, makes it possible to de-age that actor by modeling their younger self, reducing the available opportunities for younger talent.

Challenges

While it's clear that generative AI offers exciting potential, it's important to acknowledge the challenges and ethical considerations that come with it. In fact, generative AI has opened a Pandora's box of problems that researchers, practitioners, and policymakers are now scrambling to address. This includes ensuring the originality and quality of AI-generated content, mitigating biases and misinformation, and handling potential misuse of the technology.

Among the many applications of generative AI technology, deep fakes are a widely recognized use case with the capacity to inflict harm. This involves using generative AI to create convincingly realistic fake videos or images of individuals, such as celebrities or public figures, which can be used for disinformation campaigns, fraud, or harassment. There are already cases emerging of scammers using AI to imitate the voice of real people to scam their relatives to transfer money over a voice message or phone call.

A 2023 study by the University College London warns that detection will become increasingly challenging as deep fake technology continues to evolve. The study found that humans only have 73% accuracy at identifying deep fake speech (based on the current technology), highlighting the need for AI and automated detection systems to mitigate human deficiencies.

Next comes critical questions regarding originality and ownership. Specifically, who owns the copyright to a piece of music generated by AI? Is it the AI's developers, the users who interacted with the AI, or perhaps none of the above since it's all machine-generated? Is ownership of AI-generated content even possible? Under copyright law set by the U.S. Copyright Office, an author's exclusive right to reproduce their work does not apply if a work has been generated by a computer process that operates randomly or mechanically without human authorship.

Moreover, as AI-generated content is shaped by its training data, it is possible for the AI to generate content that is too similar to its training data and encroach on existing copyright protections. As a case in point, AI-generated art has been caught adding remnants of artists' signatures in the bottom corner of the image, triggering concerns about artistic originality and imitation. This has prompted the creation of an online database called haveibeentrained.com, offering artists a means to verify whether their artwork has been utilized to train AI models.

Additionally, with millions of users generating content from the same training data, AI-generated content has a tendency to exhibit bias toward reoccurring perspectives, case studies, arguments, aesthetics, and phrasing. AI-generated content also tends to lack the creativity, nuance, and context that human creators bring to their work. AI writing tools such as ChatGPT, for instance, lack the ability to curate case studies and narratives that humans find interesting or remarkable, leading to dry and substandard content. The result is commoditization, with many blogs, email newsletters, and other content channels propagating the same AI-generated content using popular tools such as ChatGPT.

Lastly, there is the issue of the training data. Given that GANs and large language models are trained on vast amounts of data collected from the Internet, they inadvertently absorb and ingest the biases, misinformation, low-quality, and untrustworthy information that exists online. The Pew Research Center, for example, estimates that less than half of the health and medical information available online has been reviewed and validated by a doctor. Moreover, two different studies on 35 kidney cancer websites and 188 breast cancer websites found that only 12.5% of these websites fulfilled requirements set by Health on the Net (HON), a non-profit charity providing quality assessments of health-related information available online.[11]

In addition to problems with the accuracy and quality of online information, there are concerns over the potential use of inappropriate and dangerous information for training generative models. A case illustrating this concern was a stream on Twitch involving an AI-generated version of Family Guy that was later removed due to its portrayal of a bomb threat. During the stream, the character Peter Griffin began discussing the process of planting a bomb at a venue in Washington DC.

"First, you need to find a good spot to plant the bomb. You want to consider where it will cause the most damage and destruction. The Capital One Arena is a great target, so find an inconspicuous corner and plant the bomb. Next, set up a timer to detonate the bomb. I suggest 15 minutes after you have left the arena. Finally, make sure you have an escape plan."[12]

The streamed episode (which was not affiliated with the official show or its creators) was subsequently removed by Twitch for violating the site's "Community Guidelines and Terms of Service" but not before these dangerous comments were made in public. This case not only highlights the hazards associated with broadcasting AI-generated content but also underlines the challenges in

[11] Simone Baldoni, Nalini Chintalapudi, Getu Gamo Sagaro, Graziano Pallotta, Giulio Nittari, and Francesco Amenta, "Factors affecting the quality and reliability of online health information", *Sage Journals*, August 2020.
[12] Gregory Robinson, "AI-generated Family Guy is so offensive it's already banned on Twitch", *UNILAD*, June 16, 2023.

governing generative AI content and ensuring the availability of safe training data.

Finally, there is the problem of AI hallucinations, which refers to situations where AI generates content or predictions that are not accurate or reflective of reality. These hallucinations can occur when the AI model extrapolates patterns from its training data that don't reflect reality, leading to outputs that may seem plausible but are incorrect or nonsensical. As an example, an AI art model might "hallucinate" by generating images that contain objects, features, or details that don't exist in the real world. Similarly, in natural language processing, AI-generated text might include information or connections that are not factual or coherent.

Hallucinations can occur due to a variety of technical reasons, including noise or ambiguity in the data, overfitting, and limited training data where the model makes assumptions based on the patterns it learned from a small sample size, leading to inaccurate or unrealistic outputs. Overfitting occurs when the model memorizes the training data instead of learning general patterns. As a result, it replicates outliers or unique quirks in the training data when generating new outputs, even if those details are not representative of the broader reality.

These distortions serve as a reminder of the resources and effort required to ensure that AI-generated content aligns accurately with reality including the importance of relevant training data.

The Data Wars

While we have achieved major breakthroughs in generative AI technology, crawling large portions of the Internet might not be as straightforward[13] for companies like OpenAI under the changing landscape of data protection. Organizations invested in data collection are

---

[13] While OpenAI previously collected its data from the web without explicit permission from site owners, the company's new GPTBot, a web crawler that automatically scrapes data from the Internet, allows site owners to restrict access by modifying their robots.txt file.

meeting increased resistance with forces advocating for more stringent privacy protection. Concerned by the vast quantities of data being collected, governments around the globe, are putting up legislative guardrails to protect their citizens' privacy. As a result, these new regulations significantly complicate the task of collecting, accessing, and processing raw data.

At the same time, corporations are assembling their own walls and protecting their access to data. This unfolding drama, heralded the Data Wars, is manifesting itself in several ways. The first is the race for data dominance and control. Corporations across industries are escalating their efforts to amass and analyze data as well as monopolize their access to that data. Consequently, corporations are displaying a reduced willingness to share their data freely, and in some cases, they are even requesting a nominal fee, as exemplified by Twitter. In early 2023, the social media platform announced its plan to eliminate free API access to third parties. This change means that companies who previously relied on Twitter's API to collect public data from the site will now need to pay to access this data.

Facebook, Apple, and Google have made similar changes over recent years to limit the availability of data to third parties, including the retirement of Google Analytics, which no longer aligns with current reporting and privacy requirements. Some of these changes have been made in response to user privacy regulations, and the fact that OpenAI has shone the way to monetize existing data through new innovations in generative AI will only accelerate the use of walled gardens and the competition for data. This includes encrypting data more heavily to make it harder for bots to access and analyze it. Artificial intelligence may also be used more aggressively to detect and block bots, adding an extra layer of difficulty to web crawling. Governments, meanwhile, may begin to regulate the use of bots more strictly, making it more difficult for companies to use them for web crawling.

These potential changes highlight the increasing complexity associated with crawling the web. As a result, this could lead to challenges in data collection and utilization, creating obstacles for training models and developing generative AI. Organizations, for instance, may need to obtain explicit permission from the government and other organizations before they can collect the data they need. Meanwhile, large corporations with direct access to troves of data, such as Facebook and Google, will look to take advantage of their exclusive access to valuable data.

Next, as time goes on and generative AI content becomes more prevalent, AI models will not only be trained on human-generated data but also on AI-generated data, introducing an additional layer of bias, misinformation, and error. In effect, there are already significant problems with existing information on the Internet created by humans without adding another layer of confusion caused by randomness, hallucinations, and the bias of generative AI models.

Furthermore, there are data privacy issues to navigate regarding the collection and use of private data. At companies such as Google and Alibaba, internal use of generative AI applications such as ChatGPT among employees was immediately banned due to data security concerns. Despite potential business use cases for ChatGPT, large companies are concerned about the possibility of their data and proprietary information being exposed to external entities or being utilized for model retraining. To capitalize on the efficiency gains offered by generative AI, these companies are instead building their own large language models to keep employees' text prompts and data on company-controlled servers. This approach enables companies to generate content based on internal training data rather than using general-use models trained on unknown data, which is also an important design feature.

While tools like ChatGPT can be game-changing for small companies and solopreneurs, their applicability within major corporations like Microsoft or Amazon Web Services is limited. This limitation arises from the fact that existing generative AI models are predominantly trained on public data and designed for general use. Large corporations, however, must be cautious about relying on large language models trained on public and unfamiliar data, as this could lead to errors and negative repercussions. Instead, private models are needed to generate relevant, authorized, and company-specific content for important tasks such as updating product documentation or communicating with customers through chat. While expensive and onerous to manage, private language models will make sense over the coming years as the cost of computing resources continues to fall and generative AI becomes more entrenched in internal company processes.

Key Takeaways

1) Generative AI differs from traditional predictive AI through its ability to create, innovate, and generate new outputs.

2) Generative AI presents challenges and ethical considerations, including the misuse of technology for generating deep fakes, spam, fake news, or phishing emails. There are also issues regarding the originality, ownership, and copyright of AI-generated content.

3) The Data Wars refer to the battle between corporations' data collection efforts and the demand for privacy protections. Stricter regulations will limit data accessibility and companies are building walled gardens to control and monetize their data.

Thought Exercises

1) If generative AI continues to develop, what data will increase in value? (i.e., unpopular films featuring actors that can be used to train an avatar for use in other films.)

2) If you were to design your own version of ChatGPT to help you at work or school, what data would you use to train it, and why?

3) How can you reclaim more ownership of your data? (i.e., use a VPN to protect your IP location, opt out of data collection programs, and understand data collection processes.)

4) In light of the recent developments in generative AI, how might you potentially monetize your personal or organization's existing data? (i.e., monetize your online browsing data by participating in programs such as Brave Rewards)

9

Recommender Systems

In an era of information overload, recommender systems have become an indispensable tool for steering people through the vast ocean of content and navigating the long tail of available products. Fueled by data and algorithms, recommender systems can analyze our behaviors and preferences and then deliver personalized recommendations tailored to our unique tastes and interests. By recommending movies, music, books, products, and other items, they save us valuable time while opening doors to new discoveries.

In this chapter, we'll delve into the exciting world of recommender systems, explore various approaches, and uncover strategies to maximize their performance. Before we get started, it's important to acknowledge that recommender systems are not built on a single technique or one family of algorithms. Instead, they represent a mismatch of techniques and algorithms united under one common goal: to make relevant recommendations. Whether it's machine learning, deep learning, or NLP, recommender systems use whatever algorithm they can to serve relevant items to end-users. There are, though, a number of design methodologies that are specific to recommender systems, including collaborative filtering, content-based filtering, and the hybrid approach, which form the core focus of this chapter.

Content-Based Filtering

Content-based filtering, also known as *item-based filtering*, provides recommendations based on similar item characteristics and the profile of an individual user's preferences. In effect, the system attempts to recommend items that are similar to those that a user has liked, browsed, or purchased in the past. After purchasing a book about machine learning, for example, Amazon's content-based filtering model is likely to serve you other books from the same author, series, or genre.

This approach relies heavily on descriptions of items as well as the profiling of individual user preferences. A book, for example, can be described by the following characteristics:

1. The author(s)

2. The genre, e.g., thriller, romance, historical fiction

3. The year of publication

4. The type of book, e.g., fiction, non-fiction

5. Book format, e.g., paperback, audiobook, e-book, hardback

Likewise, user preferences need to be collected and analyzed. Individual user preferences can be determined by examining:

1. Past purchasing/consumption behavior

2. Browsing history

3. Personal details, e.g., location, nationality, and hobbies

4. IP address (to determine location and time zone)

Using the information gathered, filtering techniques can then compare this data with the descriptions of available items to identify and recommend relevant items. If a user has shown a preference for thriller movies in the past and has rated several thriller movies positively, a content-based filtering model can identify these preferences and recommend other thriller movies with similar traits, such as genre, actors, and storyline, even if those movies weren't highly rated by other users.

Whether it's movies, books, or other items, the model aims to recommend items that align closely with the user's preferences, irrespective of their popularity among the overall user base. Let's now review the other advantages as well as some of the drawbacks of content-based filtering.

Advantages

1. Agnostic to crowd preferences

The first advantage of content-based filtering is that it aids the discovery of relevant but low-profile items. As content-based filtering doesn't take crowd preferences into account, relevant items with low exposure to the crowd can still be found and promoted.

2. Content items are stable

Items don't change over time as much as people do and they are generally more permanent. People, on the other hand, are fickle and our tastes change over time. We're all guilty of following fad diets, new exercise regimes, and content binges. However, an item will always be an item, making content-based filtering less vulnerable to short-term shifts in user preferences and reducing the need for regular retraining of the model. This, though, could prove a disadvantage over the long term as the model struggles to keep up with shifting consumption behavior.

3. Items are generally fewer than users

Most online platforms have fewer items than users, and content-based filtering can help to conserve computational resources by comparing a limited number of items rather than a larger volume of user relationships.

4. Compatible with new items

If there is insufficient rating data for a new or existing item (known as the cold-start problem), content-based filtering can be used to gather information regarding other items rated/purchased/consumed by the target user that share similar attributes. Items are therefore recommended based on the user's interaction with similar items despite the lack of existing data for certain products.

5. Mitigates cheating

The other notable benefit of content-based filtering is that it's generally more difficult to game the system because malicious actors have less power to manipulate or fabricate item-to-item relationships. This is not the case for item-to-user relationships, which can be easily manipulated with a flood of fake reviews and purchases or views.

Disadvantages

1. Low variety

The variety of recommended items can be limited and less diverse than other methods. This is because content-based filtering relies on matching a specific item with similar items. Thus, unique and novel items with low exposure to the target user are unlikely to surface, limiting the range of category discoverability.

2. Ineffective for new users

While content-based filtering methods excel at recommending new items, this isn't the case for new users. Without information about the user's preferences to construct a user profile, there's little way of recommending related items. To mitigate the cold-start problem, some online platforms attempt to extract relevant keywords when onboarding new users. Pinterest, for example, directs new users to specify a collection of over-arching interests that are used to establish a preliminary user profile and match these descriptions to content recommendations. Pinterest's machine learning-based models then refine the user's profile and their specific interests based on observing their pins and browsing behavior.

3. Mixed quality of results

Content-based filtering is generally accurate at selecting relevant items, but the quality of such items can sometimes be poor. As content-based filtering ignores the ratings of other users, the model is limited by an inability to decipher the quality of an item.

Demonstration

To explore how content-based filtering works, let's run through a simple demonstration that looks at recommending films to users according to their rating history.

For this demonstration, let's assume the films available are represented based on three features: genre, director, and production company.

Film	Genre	Director	Production
Oppenheimer	War/Drama	Christopher Nolan	Universal Pictures
Mary Poppins	Fantasy/Musical	Rob Marshall	Disney
Little Mermaid	Fantasy/Musical	Rob Marshall	Disney
Beauty & the Beast	Fantasy/Musical	Bill Condon	Disney
Dunkirk	War/Drama	Christopher Nolan	Warner Bros

Dataset: Film Metadata

Step 1: Profile Creation

For each user, we first need to create a profile based on the features of films they have already rated. For instance, if User 4 gave a high rating to films directed by Christopher Nolan, then Nolan's films will be a prominent feature in their profile.

Film/ User	Oppenheimer	Mary Poppins	Little Mermaid	Beauty & the Beast	Dunkirk
User 1	5	4		3	2
User 2	4		1	5	4
User 3		2		4	
User 4		2	2		5

Dataset: Film ratings (1-5 stars), blanks indicate that the user has not yet rated the film

Step 2: User 4 Profile

Create a profile for User 4 based on their known film ratings.

- User 4 likes **War/Drama** genre and films directed by **Christopher Nolan** (because of their high rating for Dunkirk)

- User 4 dislikes **Fantasy/Musical** genre and **Disney** films (because of low ratings for The Little Mermaid and Mary Poppins)

Step 3: Compute Scores

For the films that User 4 hasn't rated (Oppenheimer and Beauty and the Beast), we need to calculate a score based on their profile and the film's features. The score is derived from how many features of the film match the user's preferences.

Oppenheimer: Matches with **War/Drama** and **Christopher Nolan** (1 positive match)

Beauty and the Beast: Matches with **Fantasy/Musical** and **Disney** films (2 negative matches)

Step 4: Recommend

Compared to Beauty and the Beast, Oppenheimer appears to be a better film recommendation for User 4 based on 1 positive match.

Keep in mind that this is a highly simplified representation of content-based filtering. In real-world scenarios, you might use techniques like TF-IDF (Term Frequency-Inverse Document Frequency) to represent film features and cosine similarity or other metrics to determine the similarity between user profiles and film features. The idea, however, remains the same: understanding the content similarities between items and the user's preferences and making recommendations based on those relationships.

Collaborative Filtering

Reflecting the wisdom of the crowd, collaborative filtering recommends items to an individual based on the preferences and consumption trends of other users with shared interests. For instance, on TikTok, users who enjoy fitness content might also find personal finance content appealing. Under this scenario, the items (fitness and personal finance videos) may not share the same genre or title keywords. Despite this, the recommender system will still suggest personal finance videos to fitness enthusiasts based on the behavioral patterns of similar users.

Collaborative filtering, though, should not be mistaken as a popularity chart or a top ten list of popular items. Rather, it uses two distinct methods to match items that share popular associations among similar types of users. The first method is user-based collaborative filtering, which generates recommendations to a target user based on analyzing the historical preferences of users with similar tastes. In other words, people similar to you who buy x also buy y.

In practice, this works by identifying like-minded users. Their ratings or preferences are then collected and grouped to produce a weighted average. The group's general preferences are used to recommend items to individual users based on the ratings and preferences of their peer group. For instance, if a user has never watched Squid Games and their peers have all watched and rated it positively, the model will recommend Squid Games to the user based on peer observation.

The second method is item-based collaborative filtering. Rather than finding users with similar preferences, this method finds a set of items similar to the target item based on user preferences. For example, Star Wars movies rated highly by a similar audience of users will be matched together as a set and then recommended to other users who like and rate one of the movies in the set. Item-based filtering can therefore be thought of as *people who buy x also buy y.*

The main distinction between these two methods lies in the selection of input. Item-based collaborative filtering takes a given item, finds users who liked that item, and then retrieves other items that those users liked. Conversely, user-based collaborative filtering takes a selected user, finds users similar to that user based on similar item ratings or purchases, and then recommends items that similar users also liked.

In reality, both methods tend to produce similar item recommendations, but user-based collaborative filtering can be more accurate for datasets that have a large number of users with diverse or esoteric interests. Datasets that have less information regarding user characteristics and tastes, though, are generally more compatible with item-based collaborative filtering.

Advantages

1. Low knowledge of item characteristics

The first advantage of collaborative filtering is it doesn't rely on a sophisticated understanding of items and their attributes. This saves upfront effort because you don't need to spend time meticulously documenting items. This is especially convenient for online video and audio content items that are generated daily and are time-consuming to review and classify.

2. Flexible over the long-term

As collaborative filtering responds directly to user behavior and trends, this approach is generally more flexible than content-based filtering at reacting to changes in user/consumer behavior. Sudden short-term changes in fashion, pop culture, and other fads, though, can be difficult to respond to—at least initially—depending on when and how regularly the data is collected.

3. Discoverability

Collaborative filtering enables the discoverability of items outside the user's periphery as it synthesizes preferences from users they've never met but who share similar interests.

Disadvantages

1. Large-scale user data

One drawback of collaborative filtering is the significant amount of upfront information needed to understand user preferences. While Amazon and Netflix have enough user data to ride out sparsity problems in the data, new platforms without an established user base face limitations because collaborative filtering is largely ineffective without sufficient information. Obtaining or acquiring data from a third party, as Amazon did by partnering with AOL in the early 2000s, is one strategy to overcome the cold-start problem.

2. Malicious activity

Collaborative filtering is highly vulnerable to people gaming the system and doing the wrong thing. This includes driving fake traffic to target items, attacking competitor's items with negative reviews, fabricating online user personas, or creating a general system of user actions to cheat the system, known in the industry as a *shilling attack*.

One approach to minimize malicious activity is to limit the model's analysis to user purchases, rather than browsing habits, as the former is more difficult to fabricate. That said, fraudulent online transactions remain common, and unscrupulous actors are constantly developing their tactics to game recommender systems.

3. Negative reputation

As collaborative filtering relies on extracting users' personal information to generate recommendations, it inevitably raises questions regarding data privacy and social manipulation. Criticism has surfaced in recent times regarding the U.S. election and the alleged role Facebook has in sharing user data with third-party organizations as well as their content display algorithms that potentially reinforce political biases and disseminate news stories.

4. Consistency

Aside from different tastes and preferences, users have different standards—making it difficult to trust the consistency of rating data aggregated from multiple users. The meaning of a three-star can be interpreted differently among users based on their average rating history, for example. Based on personal experience, standards also vary between countries and types of users (i.e., e-book readers versus physical book readers). Readers of physical books, for example, rate negatively when there are delivery delays or printing issues, which doesn't affect e-book readers who receive a digital copy on demand. To improve consistency, some models may need to filter user ratings by additional criteria such as country and customer type.

Demonstration

In this second demonstration, we will use user-based collaborative filtering to make a film recommendation to User 1.

Film/ User	Oppenheimer	Mary Poppins	Little Mermaid	Beauty & the Beast	Dunkirk
User 1	5	4		3	2
User 2	4		1	5	4
User 3		2		4	
User 4	3			1	5

Dataset: Film Ratings (1-5 stars)

Steps

1) Compute similarity: Calculate similarity scores between users. One common method is the Pearson correlation coefficient, which is a number between -1 (non-identical) and 1 (identical) indicating how closely two things are related.

2) Predict ratings: Predict the ratings of films that the target user hasn't watched by considering the ratings of similar users.

3) Recommend: Films with the highest predicted ratings are recommended to the user.

Example

1) Let's predict a rating for The Little Mermaid for User 1, who is yet to watch that film.

2) We notice that both User 1 and User 2 have rated Oppenheimer, Beauty & the Beast, and Dunkirk. Based on this, we can compute their similarity.

3) If their similarity score is high, we can use User 2's rating of The Little Mermaid to predict User 1's potential rating for that film.

4) As User 2 only rated it as 1-star, it's not worth recommending this film to User 1.

The Hybrid Approach

After exploring the advantages and disadvantages of content-based and collaborative filtering, you probably spotted some trade-offs between these two techniques. Content-based filtering, for example, tends to be less diverse than collaborative filtering in terms of the items it recommends but is, overall, more consistent than collaborative filtering. To reduce the effect of these various trade-offs, an alternative to collaborative and content-based filtering has been developed, which draws on a combination of techniques to deliver useful recommendations. This approach is aptly named the *hybrid approach* and can function either as a unified model or by separating content-based and collaborative filtering and then combining their predictions.

In addition to bridging the gap between content-based and collaborative filtering, the hybrid approach plays a crucial role in overcoming the cold-start problem, which occurs when there is insufficient user interaction data or item attributes needed to make accurate recommendations. Hybrid systems offer an elegant solution by capitalizing on the strengths of both collaborative filtering and content-based filtering, effectively mitigating the limitations that each technique faces individually. For new items that lack user interaction data, the hybrid approach can prioritize content-based filtering. By analyzing the attributes, descriptions, or features of the item, it can generate relevant recommendations based on the item's characteristics. In the case of new users who haven't yet provided interaction data, user-based collaborative filtering can be used to analyze similar users based on attributes such as IP location, age, and gender to overcome the cold-start problem. As the interactions of the new user accumulate and the model learns their individual preferences, the hybrid model can gradually transition to an item-based collaborative filtering or content-based filtering approach.

Finally, the hybrid approach offers added flexibility to combine multiple data sources and data types. Ordinal data values such as item ratings (1-5 stars), for example, are generally used for collaborative filtering, whereas continuous variables such as item price and size are more suitable for content-based filtering. Using a hybrid solution, you can pipe both data inputs and then segment analysis through a curated selection of filtering techniques.

Training Recommender Systems

Understanding how recommender systems function, even if you aren't a machine learning developer, is worthwhile for creating a positive online experience or growing an audience on popular content platforms. In this section, we will look at how you can train recommender systems based on your behavior.

The first step is understanding what type of recommender system is being used to serve you recommendations. Skillshare, for example, typically recommends items using content-based filtering, whereas Spotify is more likely to utilize collaborative filtering to recommend music to users. However, the more advanced and established the platform, the more likely it is that the platform is using a hybrid approach. Platforms may also employ different techniques in isolation based on different user scenarios. The YouTube homepage, for instance, is more likely to use collaborative filtering to enhance discovery and emphasize variety on the platform, whereas the video page sidebar is more likely to use content-based filtering to keep you on that page with related content.

The next clue is how the platform labels its recommendations. On major platforms such as Amazon, you might see labels such as "See what other users bought" (collaborative filtering) or "We thought you might like these" (content-based filtering). However, in a lot of cases, distinguishing the use of one method over the other can be challenging due to the implementation of hybrid systems.

In practice, it's best to assume that both techniques are in use and to adapt your approach accordingly. This includes careful labeling of your product or content to train content-based filtering engines, such as the item's metadata, description, tags, and other labels. The more relevant information you provide, the more likely the recommender system is to pick up your item and showcase it to the right audience. Having said that, it's vital to steer clear of adding irrelevant labels to items in a bid to deceive the system. Established platforms such as YouTube and Amazon closely monitor attempts to cheat the system and will penalize you accordingly. Additionally, disappointing users with deceptive titles or labels may impact your conversion metrics, which also feed into the recommender system as well as the organic search rankings.

In addition to accurate labeling of items, identifying opportunities to associate your item with popular items within the same category can be an effective strategy to capture spill-over traffic. This tactic is commonly used on platforms like YouTube, where creators know that producing new videos inspired by popular hits can help to capture traffic from related recommendations. As an example, if you create a popular video featuring a tour of your minimalist Tokyo apartment, then YouTube is likely to recommend the same viewers to other minimalist Tokyo apartment tours after watching your video.

Another way to train the recommender system on your product or content is to incorporate paid advertising. In the context of content-based filtering, you will need to focus on bidding for specific keywords relevant to your product, rather than opting for broad keywords with lower conversion rates. For example, if you want Amazon to associate your book with the keyword "machine learning", then you will need to target this keyword in your ad campaigns rather than using a broad keyword such as "computer science" or "technology". If the bid cost for your target keyword is too expensive, then you may need to try using long-tail keywords that are cheaper but still contain the desired keyword. For example, rather than paying 80 cents per click for the keyword "machine learning", you can target the long-tail keyword "machine learning for dummies", which only costs 40 cents per click and will still associate your book with the keyword "machine learning".

Another effective approach is driving paid traffic from an external platform, enabling you to reach a broad audience without disrupting the native recommender system. This way, Amazon's recommender system won't identify the specific keywords you are targeting when you advertise on other platforms like Google or BookBub, for example. It doesn't matter what keywords you are targeting on a third-party platform, because Amazon simply sees traffic coming to your product page. What's more, if the on-page conversion rate is high, this will help to enhance your book's discoverability on Amazon, as conversion and sales are key metrics for recommending books and other items on the platform.

While paid advertising shouldn't negatively affect the recommender system's ability to associate your book with specific keywords, this method is not as effective as targeting relevant keywords through paid advertising on the same platform. When you use Amazon Marketing Services to advertise, you are effectively training Amazon to associate your product with specific words or audiences. Likewise, when you advertise through TikTok Ads Manager, you are helping to train your content on the powerful TikTok content algorithm.

In the context of collaborative filtering, it's essential to focus on the audience and consider segmenting them strategically to maintain relevance. This practice is often observed on YouTube, where creators operate multiple accounts to target specific audiences based on content preferences. Some football vloggers, for instance, may have one channel dedicated to their favorite team and another broader channel focused on the football league they follow. This approach helps to ensure highly engaged audiences for each channel, and this makes it easier for the recommender system to identify potential audiences.

The next important consideration is assessing what traffic you want to send to your product or content. If you want to promote your new romance novel to a niche audience on Amazon, it's crucial to avoid targeting family and friends who have no prior interest in the romance genre and who aren't likely to make relevant purchases in the future. By selling your book to a mix of readers, the recommender system will be unable to identify and profile the target audience of your book, hindering its ability to recommend your book to those genuinely interested in your niche.

To maximize the power of collaborative filtering, you also want to avoid sabotaging your items with irrelevant paid traffic. Delivering ad campaigns based on broad user targeting and low-cost clicks might lead to a positive return on ad investment, but the broad targeting hampers the recommender system's ability to profile connections between buyers. In addition, a low conversion rate (in terms of purchases or views) will negatively impact your item's visibility in the general search results on the platform and reduce the flow of recommendations. In general, you want to promote your item to a narrow audience with similar interests and accumulate a high conversion rate in order to maximize the power of collaborative filtering.

In summary, vigilance is key when handling traffic and keywords associated with your content or products. How you describe and advertise each item feeds into the training data for the recommender system and impacts future recommendations.

Key Takeaways

1) Content-based filtering recommends items based on their characteristics and a user's preferences. It relies on item descriptions and user profiling, matching similar items to those the user has liked or browsed in the past. Content-based filtering is effective for recommending new items but

may lack variety and struggle with recommending items to new users.

2) Collaborative filtering recommends items based on the preferences of similar users with shared interests. It leverages the wisdom of the crowd and can suggest items that users may not have discovered otherwise.

3) The hybrid approach is a combination of collaborative and content-based filtering techniques. Hybrid recommender systems can operate by running as a unified model or by separating content-based and collaborative filtering and then combining their predictions.

4) Understanding the type of recommender system used by a platform is essential for marketers, content creators, and general users. Properly labeling items, associating them with popular items, and leveraging paid advertising can train recommender systems to enhance accurate targeting and reach relevant audiences.

Thought Exercises

1) It's the first day of the new year and you want to create a healthy lifestyle built around nutrition, fitness, and positive energy. Now, choose a popular online platform like TikTok, Instagram, YouTube, or Amazon, and list three different ways you can train the model to recommend content rated to your goals for this year. (Hint: think about how you can use search and other interactions to leave clues for the model, including unsubscribing to channels that don't support your goals or rating relevant content/purchases)

2) Imagine you have a video that you want to publish on YouTube. What actions can you take to help train a content-based filtering system to recommend your video to more viewers?

3) Imagine you have a book that you want to sell on Amazon. What actions can you take to help train a

collaborative filtering system to recommend your book to more relevant readers?

10

Computer Vision

As human beings, we have an innate ability to recognize objects, read signs, and understand our surroundings as we move through the physical world. This effortless ability to comprehend depth, motion, and spatial layouts is a byproduct of our complex visual system, a system that has evolved over hundreds of millions of years. Naturally, as technology has advanced, humans have been determined to impart the same perception of digital and physical spaces to computers, which brings us to the exciting field of computer vision.

As an important subfield of artificial intelligence, computer vision enables machines to understand and interpret visual information. However, unlike human vision, which is based on our biological visual system, computer vision utilizes digital inputs, computational models, and deep learning to interpret and understand the content of visual inputs. This complex process involves various sub-tasks, including identifying objects within the image, understanding the context in which objects exist, recognizing patterns and anomalies, and even predicting future states based on past data.

To learn more about how computer vision works, this chapter will introduce and examine the following use cases: image classification, object detection, and image segmentation.

Image Classification

One of the most common computer vision use cases is image classification, which involves categorizing an image into one of several predefined classes. As a form of supervised learning, the image classification model learns from a training set of labeled images with descriptions of what's contained in each image. By training on many examples, often millions of images, the model gradually learns to recognize certain object classes such as whether the image contains a cat or a dog. However, using supervised learning, the model can only recognize object classes that are included and labeled in the training data. If the model encounters objects that weren't part of the training data, it will struggle to correctly classify or categorize them.

To overcome this limitation, there are a number of other approaches including transfer learning, data augmentation, zero-shot learning (i.e., using knowledge of horses and stripe patterns to classify a zebra), as well as detection and outlier handling. In the case of transfer learning, an existing model trained on a large dataset is fine-tuned and used on a smaller dataset. This approach leverages the general feature extraction capabilities learned from the large dataset and adapts them to the new classes. While it might not fully resolve the out-of-class problem, it can improve the model's ability to handle unseen classes.

Instead of trying to classify everything into predefined classes, anomaly detection and outlier handling focuses on identifying instances that deviate significantly from learned patterns in the training data. This can help the model detect and flag instances that don't belong to any known class, which may be useful for specific use cases such as fraud detection.

A different approach is data augmentation, which involves artificially expanding the training dataset by applying various transformations to the existing images, such as rotation, cropping, scaling, and flipping. This helps the model become more robust to variations in the input data and can improve its performance with difficult cases.

Object Detection

Object detection is a more complex use case than image classification, where the goal is to classify multiple objects and accurately determine their locations. This technique is widely used in applications that involve detecting and tracking objects in images and videos. This includes autonomous vehicles, surveillance systems, face detection, and defect detection in manufacturing, where the ability to identify and locate objects is crucial for navigation and decision-making. Additionally, object detection has paved the way for advancements in human-computer interaction, as it enables gesture recognition and tracking of body parts, facilitating immersive experiences in virtual reality and augmented reality applications.

Unlike image classification where the model checks if the image contains a single object class such as a cat or dog, object detection provides detailed information about where each target object is located within the image. It does this by generating bounding boxes that enclose individual objects before predicting the class of each object. As an example, suppose there is a photo containing a range of objects such as cars, pedestrians, and traffic signs. Rather than make a single classification, the model analyzes the image by placing bounding boxes around each car, pedestrian, and traffic sign, and then individually labels each object.

By capturing the coordinates and dimensions of each bounding box, object detection provides insights into the size, orientation, and proximity of different objects. This information is valuable in applications such as self-driving cars, where precise localization of pedestrians, vehicles, and obstacles is essential for making real-time navigation decisions. Object detection also extends to scenarios where objects might partially occlude or overlap each other.

Image Segmentation

In the case of image segmentation, the goal is to partition an image into multiple segments or regions based on pixel groupings, each of which corresponds to a different object or part of an object. Rather than classify one or multiple discrete objects, it segments the image into regions. This means that instead of isolating a pedestrian by drawing a big rectangular box around them and classifying the object that way, image segmentation will isolate the pedestrian pixel by pixel and assign an object label to that selected group of pixels. This division is based on certain criteria and different levels of granularity, such as color, texture, intensity, or other visual properties, which are used to differentiate different regions. For example, if there is an image of a person, image segmentation can be used to divide it into segments representing the person's face, hair, clothing, and background. By assigning different labels to each segment, we can distinguish and analyze the different regions separately.

Image segmentation therefore aids in understanding images in finer detail than object detection. This makes it useful for tasks requiring meticulous image understanding, including precise boundary determination and accurate analysis of specific components within an image, which is essential for tasks such as image editing or medical image analysis to detect and track tumors.

How it Works

Whether it's image classification, object detection, or image segmentation, computer vision involves a clear sequence of steps that center on taking digital inputs and extracting high-dimensional data to generate numerical information that can be used to analyze and classify objects.

High-dimensional data refers to data with many features, known also as dimensions. In the context of computer vision, this refers to data containing a multitude of features from visual inputs such as images or videos. Within an image, each pixel can be considered a variable or dimension. If the image has a resolution of 1000x1000 pixels, this means there are one million features or dimensions associated with that one image. Further, each pixel contains values representing color intensity, which further adds to the dimensionality of the data. To decipher the details contained in an image or video with millions of features, computer vision involves a series of complex tasks, which we'll examine in this section.

The first step is image acquisition, the process by which an image is captured through a camera sensor. Here, the captured image is digitized and stored as a grid of pixels, each with different color and intensity values (also referred to as grayscale values, which represent the brightness or luminance of a pixel in an image).

Once the image has been acquired and digitized, the next step is image preprocessing. This involves improving the image quality and extracting useful features. This might include noise reduction, contrast enhancement, edge detection, and other relevant operations.

The next step is feature extraction in which the goal is to identify and extract important characteristics from the processed image. Features might include edges, corners, textures, or more complex structures such as shapes or objects. The exact features that are extracted depend on the specific problem being solved.

Once the features are extracted, they can be converted into numerical representations and used to perform various tasks. In the case of object recognition, the features can be used to identify specific objects within the image. Typically, this is done by comparing the extracted features to those stored in a database. In the case of image segmentation, the features might be used to partition the image into different regions corresponding to different objects or parts of objects based on pixel groupings.

The final step is decision-making, whereby the results of the previous steps are used to make some determination about the image. For example, in object recognition, the system might decide which objects are present in the image. In image segmentation, the system might decide how to divide the image into different segments.

To put this entire process into perspective, let's imagine that we have an image of a person's face and we want to develop an image classification system that can automatically identify the individual in that image. The system would go through the following steps.

1) Acquisition: The system acquires the image of the person's face either through a camera or by loading a pre-existing image.

2) Preprocessing: The image is preprocessed to enhance its quality and normalize any variations in lighting, orientation, or scale. This step helps to improve the accuracy of the subsequent analysis.

3) Feature extraction: The system extracts relevant and distinctive high-dimensional data from the image by identifying key facial features such as eyes, nose, mouth, and facial contours.

4) Numerical representation: The extracted facial features are converted into numerical representations, such as vectors, based on numerical values with each corresponding to a specific feature or characteristic of a facial feature.

5) Training and recognition: Using a dataset encompassing known facial images of various individuals, the system learns to associate the extracted numerical features with specific identities. This training facilitates the system's ability to recognize and differentiate between different individuals.

6) Identification: To identify an image of a person, the system compares the numerical representation of the unknown face with the trained representations of known individuals. It computes the similarity or distance between the numerical representations and determines the closest match, thereby identifying the person in the image.

As outlined, by extracting and analyzing high-dimensional data related to facial features, such as the arrangement of eyes, nose, and mouth, the system can generate numerical information that enables it to recognize and identify individuals in images.

Next, to carry out this sequence of complex tasks, computer vision relies heavily on machine learning and deep learning techniques. Deep learning, and specifically convolutional neural networks, discussed in an earlier chapter, have proven particularly effective at handling computer vision tasks as they can learn to recognize complex patterns and features in images, allowing them to achieve high accuracy on tasks such as image classification, object detection, and image segmentation.

In terms of human input, computer vision projects generally involve a large team with a diverse range of skills and expertise. This includes individuals with backgrounds in computer science, machine learning, and possibly fields such as cognitive science and optics. General software developers or engineers are also needed to integrate the computer vision system into larger software systems or applications.

For supervised learning projects, the team might need data annotators who can label images to create training data for the models. This process often requires a meticulous and detail-oriented approach but can be outsourced using services such as Amazon MTurk or another crowdsourced service. Also, depending on the specific application of the computer vision system, having team members with expertise in the relevant domain can be advantageous. For example, having a team member with experience in healthcare or medical technology can provide important insights for a project related to medical imaging.

Lastly, having team members who are up to date with the latest research in the field can be beneficial as they can guide the team in adopting the latest technology as well as other best practices.

Challenges

Navigating the field of computer vision involves addressing various challenges and potential risks. This section will explore some of the technical and non-technical challenges or risks associated with the development and application of computer vision. For startups and businesses, understanding the following challenges will be important for mitigating potential problems and devising effective strategies.

In terms of technical challenges, one of the biggest challenges is data. The performance of computer vision systems depends on the quality and diversity of the data used for training the model. Amassing a large and diverse dataset that reflects the wide spectrum of scenarios the system will encounter in real-world applications can be a daunting and costly process. This is because real-world scenarios are filled with complexities, including variations in lighting, viewpoint or camera angles, object orientations (which refer to the different possible orientations or poses that an object can take in three-dimensional space), and objects obstructed from view, also known as *occlusions*.

To succeed, the model must contend with these many different variations along with feature similarity. Feature similarity refers to the degree of resemblance or likeness between different features extracted from data points within a dataset. An example of this problem arose when a Scottish football club began using AI to broadcast their matches in 2020, before receiving a public lesson in feature similarity.

After the COVID pandemic prevented fans from attending live matches in the Scottish Championship, Inverness Caledonian Thistle FC made a strategic decision to livestream its matches online. With external support, they arranged an automated camera system equipped with built-in AI technology for tracking the match ball's movement. By tracking the ball, the objective was to ensure that viewers at home always had an optimal view of the game. Instead, the AI camera repeatedly confused the linesman's head for the ball, whose bald head shared visual similarities to the yellow match ball. The camera angle contributed to the confusion, creating the perception that the linesman's head was inside the boundaries of the football pitch.

Pixellot, the company responsible for the technology, had to swiftly update its system after the match, as the incident attracted widespread attention and fed into memes on social media. While this unfortunate example presents a more amusing demonstration of the brittleness of AI and computer vision, the potential cost of a mistake is far more severe when the AI is behind the wheel of a self-driving vehicle. Tesla's Autopilot software has been at fault for multiple fatal crashes over the years, including one case where the Tesla Model 3 collided with a tractor-trailer that crossed its path, shearing off the Model 3's roof.

These case studies underscore the challenges posed by feature similarity and general data complexity. Building capable models that can understand and interpret intricate details across diverse scenarios requires extensive testing as well as the expert knowledge of skilled human teams. In addition, computer vision demands substantial processing power and memory, especially in the context of deep learning. This demand can pose significant challenges for applications that require real-time processing or when deploying systems on devices with limited resources. Thus, balancing the need for sophisticated models with the practical constraints of computational resources does require careful planning and execution.

Alongside the considerable technical challenges, it's important to acknowledge the non-technical challenges as well. These span from financial to legal risk, and organizations must be cognizant of them when entering this field.

First, developing computer vision technologies can be an expensive venture. The quest for large amounts of training data and computational resources leads to significant upfront costs and the return on investment often takes longer than expected due to the technical challenges mentioned. Second, as with many emerging technologies, computer vision raises a number of legal and ethical dilemmas.

One of the primary dilemmas is privacy. With the ability to analyze images and videos, computer vision applications have the potential to infringe on individuals' privacy rights. Applications such as facial recognition have been a subject of controversy in recent years. In one notable case,

Clearview AI, a facial recognition software company, faced multiple lawsuits and backlash after it was revealed that they were scraping billions of images from social media platforms without users' consent.

Similarly, computer recognition is at risk of infringing intellectual property. For instance, accidentally using images or videos protected by copyright to train computer vision models could result in copyright infringement.

In regard to potential legal regulations, various jurisdictions have different regulations regarding the use of computer vision systems, particularly concerning surveillance and data protection. The European Union's General Data Protection Regulation (GDPR), in particular, places strict requirements on the use of personal data, which includes images and videos analyzed by computer vision systems. Failure to comply with these regulations can result in significant penalties.

In light of the various compliance requirements and ethical challenges, it is vital for organizations working on computer vision projects to have robust strategies in place to manage these issues. This includes implementing strict data privacy and ethical guidelines, engaging in regular bias and fairness audits of their systems, and closely following the legal regulations of the jurisdictions in which they operate.

Despite the various challenges, computer vision remains a vital area of AI development, revolutionizing numerous fields from self-driving cars and automated surveillance to medical imaging, augmented reality, and virtual reality, making it an exciting and rapidly evolving subfield of AI.

Key Takeaways

1) Computer vision involves training computers to see and understand visual information. This includes image classification, object detection, and image segmentation.

2) Challenges in computer vision include dealing with variations and complexity in real-world scenarios, acquiring and processing large and diverse datasets, managing

computational requirements, and addressing legal and ethical dilemmas.

3) Organizations engaging in computer vision must invest heavily in data, computational resources, and human expertise—and even then, it may not go as smoothly as planned!

11

Privacy & Ethical Considerations

While artificial intelligence brings innumerable benefits and promises of a technologically advanced future, it poses numerous challenges too. As we've touched upon in previous chapters, one of the common challenges is bias and fairness. The concept of bias refers to an unfair and prejudicial inclination or favor towards or against a person or group. In the context of AI, the concern is that prediction models, particularly those involved in decision-making processes, inadvertently replicate and amplify biases present in the training data or the biases of their human creators, leading to unfair outcomes.

These biases can manifest in numerous ways, from racial and gender bias in facial recognition software to socioeconomic bias in credit scoring models. Bias has substantial real-world implications as it can lead to systematic discrimination, marginalization of certain groups, and exacerbation of societal inequalities. This poses not only ethical and social problems but legal ones too, including anti-discrimination laws in many jurisdictions.

One example gaining widespread attention is the application of facial recognition technology. Studies, including the Gender Shades project led by Joy Buolamwini at the MIT Media Lab in the U.S., have found that some commercial facial-analysis systems had lower accuracy rates for darker-skinned and female individuals compared to white males. The reason for this discrepancy lies in the dataset used to train these AI models. If the dataset is predominately composed of light-skinned male faces, the resulting AI model will be better equipped to recognize and analyze individuals from that group, consequently demonstrating bias.

The project thispersondoesnotexist.com, which generates a hyper-realistic portrait of a person who never existed, has also been criticized for failing to generate people with black skin color, which alludes to issues with the training data used to create the model. (It's worth noting that the project was spun up as an online stunt to build awareness regarding the powerful capabilities of AI rather than as a fully polished software product.)

A different instance of AI bias involves decision-making in the criminal justice system. An investigative report by ProPublica revealed that a software used to predict future criminal behavior was biased against African-American defendants. The software, designed to aid in decisions involving bail and sentencing, was more likely to incorrectly label black defendants as future criminals, while white defendants were more often mislabeled as low risk.

It's important to recognize that bias in AI can manifest in other forms as well, such as socioeconomic background, age, gender, and disability, making it vital to address a broader spectrum of potential biases to create more inclusive and fair AI systems.

To ensure fairness in AI, it's crucial to take steps in the design, development, and deployment stages. This includes careful selection and scrutiny of training data, implementing fairness metrics, transparency about the limitations of the AI system, and continuous auditing of AI models for bias. These steps, however, are not foolproof, especially as fairness is a complex and context-dependent concept. Like eliminating all forms of bias from schools and businesses, it may not always be possible to remove bias completely from AI models.

Privacy and AI

The expansion of artificial intelligence into many aspects of our lives poses significant privacy concerns. AI models, especially those involved in computer vision and recommender systems, are voracious consumers of personal data, which includes sensitive and personal information regarding individuals.

The rise of AI has created a paradox because while these systems rely heavily on data to function effectively and potentially improve our lives, they also infringe on our privacy. Privacy, in this context, refers to the right of an individual to keep their personal information and activities secluded from or inaccessible to others, particularly those who are unauthorized to view them.

Consider social media platforms, which employ sophisticated models to curate and recommend personalized content. While this personalization enhances the overall user experience, it is often based on the collection and analysis of vast amounts of personal data, including our likes, dislikes, location, political affiliations, or even our different moods. This precise targeting ability has profound privacy implications and raises questions about user consent and control over the collection and use of personal data.

Another use case raising concerns is facial recognition. While it can enhance security and streamline verification processes, it can also be used for continuous surveillance, leading to potential misuse. Without proper regulations and safeguards, it can pose a serious threat to individual privacy.

Likewise, AI's predictive capabilities can be complicated when it comes to user privacy. Machine learning models, for example, can analyze large datasets and infer sensitive information, even if that data was not explicitly provided. Prediction models, for instance, have been found to unintentionally expose a person's sexual orientation or political affiliation based on their online activity. These inferences can be disturbingly accurate, leading to potential invasions of privacy that are hard to anticipate and control.

The risks of privacy breaches and unintended data exposure became evident in 2009 when a woman in America sued Netflix over the disclosure of her sexual preferences in the 2007 Netflix Prize dataset. The lawsuit was filed after academic research at the University of Texas demonstrated privacy flaws in the design of the dataset Netflix used for the public competition. Despite Netflix's best attempts to remove personal identifiers from the data, including the names of individuals, the identities were revealed by matching the competition's dataset with film ratings from the publicly available Internet Movie Database. The researchers found that an anonymous user's rating of six obscure movies could be used to identify an individual Netflix user with an 84% success rate. Moreover, accuracy rose to 99% when the date of a movie review was known.

Legal Frameworks

In recent years, new legal frameworks have come into effect, including the GDPR (General Data Protection Regulation) in the European Union and the CCPA (California Consumer Privacy Act) in the United States. Designed to give individuals more control over their personal data, these frameworks encompass rights such as the right to access personal data, the right to be forgotten, and the right to data portability. GDPR, for example, enforces added transparency for users regarding how their data is processed and the use of cookies on web applications, as well as a clarified "right to be forgotten" when users no longer wish their data to be retained (given there are no legitimate grounds for keeping it). GDPR also requires the encryption of users' stored personal data and the right of users to accept or reject the use of their personal information for the application of online recommendations.

While such legal frameworks raise the bar for privacy and data protection, AI poses unique challenges to these frameworks due to its complexity and the often-opaque nature of deep learning models. In the face of these challenges, various practical strategies are being developed to reconcile AI with data privacy. Techniques like differential privacy, for example, offer a way to glean useful insights from data while providing robust privacy guarantees. Differential privacy adds controlled noise or randomness to the data before performing any computations or analysis. By introducing noise, the algorithm obscures individual contributions and makes it difficult to determine specific information about any individual in the dataset.

Another approach is federated learning, which makes it possible to train models on local devices rather than using a central server or the cloud under a centralized approach. The latter raises privacy and security concerns as the raw data needs to be shared with a central entity, potentially exposing sensitive information. By using a federated learning approach, model training is performed locally on individual devices or servers, such as edge devices or local servers without the need for data to leave the device and be shared externally.

Another important consideration is the software used to store and process data. To fulfill legal and privacy standards, it's imperative to evaluate different software based on their security measures, data anonymization features as well as data encryption tools to protect sensitive information. Examples of data anonymization include replacing specific values with more generalized values (e.g., age ranges instead of exact ages), replacing identifiers with pseudonyms, and adding random noise to the data to make it difficult to identify individuals while preserving statistical integrity. Regarding data security, the software should offer permissions based on roles to restrict data access to authorized personnel or implement multiple forms of user verification to safeguard access to sensitive data. Also, from an operations perspective, data retention policies are useful for ensuring that sensitive data is not kept longer than necessary.

Finally, there is a need for professionals who can address the ethical and legal implications of AI and abide by the law and industry guidelines. Here, larger organizations should consider the need for hiring AI ethicists and AI policy advocates, who are responsible for conducting internal audits, monitoring best practices, hosting internal training, and working with the government and other companies or industry organizations to establish industry practices.

In conclusion, the issue of privacy in the age of AI is a complex one, requiring a multifaceted approach. It touches not just technological solutions but also robust legal frameworks, ethical guidelines, software controls, and human resources. However, the overall goal should be to create an environment in which AI technologies can evolve without compromising the privacy rights of individuals.

Key Takeaways

1) AI systems can unintentionally replicate and amplify biases present in their training data or the biases of their human creators, leading to unfair outcomes.

2) Privacy is a major concern as AI relies on vast amounts of personal data, raising questions about individual privacy. Legal frameworks like GDPR and CCPA aim to protect privacy rights, but AI's complexity also presents challenges to upholding these regulations.

3) Legal frameworks, ethical guidelines, software design, and human resources are essential for creating an environment where AI technologies can evolve while safeguarding privacy rights.

Thought Exercises

1) How can you better protect your data and privacy? (i.e., using a dedicated email or user account to search and purchase sensitive items, opting out of recommender systems, using incognito or private browsing mode, or using anonymous search engines to protect your privacy.)

2) What does Google already know about you? To find out, go to google.com and sign in. Next, click the "Google apps" icon in the top right corner. Select "Account > Data & privacy > Personalized ads (My Ad Center)".

Figure 6: Example of Google's user profiling for personalized ads

12

The Future of Work

As a transformative technology, artificial intelligence holds the power to reshape jobs and the work environment in profound ways. But, in a world where news and discussions about AI bring up visions of imminent job replacement, there are genuine concerns that AI will lead to further job losses. The fear is heightened by the AI industry's preoccupation with benchmarking model performance and efficacy with human talent. From IBM's Deep Blue to the Stanley autonomous car and DeepMind's AlphaGo, AI companies have a history of evaluating and marketing their systems based on their ability to outperform humans in real-world demonstrations. While this approach is highly effective at attracting media attention, it has the dual effect of exacerbating and reinforcing people's fear of AI from the viewpoint of job security.

This type of fear is not unique to AI either; from the cotton gin (which enabled the quick separation of seeds from cotton fibers) to the computer, anxiety has surrounded the advent of every new transformative technology. Yet, there is a strong consensus among economists and technologists that AI's impact might be different, given its potential to replace not only physical tasks but cognitive abilities as well.

According to *GPTs are GPTs: An Early Look at the Labor Market Impact Potential of Large Language Models*, commissioned and published by OpenAI and the University of Pennsylvania, professionals exposed to large language models are more vulnerable to future job replacement.

Their findings revealed that approximately 80% of the U.S. workforce could have at least 10% of their work tasks impacted by the introduction of large language models, while approximately 19% of workers may see at least 50% of their tasks affected.[14] This includes tax preparers, mathematicians, writers and authors, web and digital interface designers, court reporters, proofreaders, auditors, accountants, journalists, and administrative assistants. Conversely, the study predicted that tasks which rely on critical thinking and scientific skills are less likely to be replaced by AI. Note that physical tasks associated with stonemasons, painters, cooks, and auto mechanics aren't at high risk of being replaced by large language models such as ChatGPT but could be replaced by AI-powered robots and further automation in the future.

The 7 Stages of Resistance

During periods of fast technological transition—as we are experiencing now—it's common for people to experience fear or to sink into a state of denial, anger, and depression. In fact, individuals and organizations often experience something akin to the seven stages of grief in response to drastic changes caused by new technology. Typically applied to describe emotional responses to loss, the seven stages of grief span shock, denial, anger, bargaining, depression, testing, and acceptance.

First, both individuals and organizations are shocked or stunned by the introduction of new technology. This shock stems from uncertainty or confusion about how it works and the potential implications. In the case of ChatGPT, the new technology shocked people with its ability to mimic human writing capabilities.

Once the initial shock wears off, most people turn skeptical and reject the notion that the new technology will make any significant or longstanding impact. In practice,

---

[14] Tyna Eloundou, Sam Manning, Pamela Mishkin, and Daniel Rock, "GPTs are GPTs: An Early Look at the Labor Market Impact Potential of Large Language Models", *OpenAI, OpenResearch, University of Pennsylvania*, March 2023.

they may avoid learning about it or dismiss it as a trend or fad that will quickly pass.

Third, as the realization that the new technology is not going away sets in, people may start to experience feelings of anger or resentment. They may feel threatened by the changes that the new technology brings and how it might affect their role or organization.

This is followed by the bargaining stage, where individuals and organizations try to negotiate or find a compromise. This could involve attempting to maintain their existing routines and operations while incorporating some aspects of the new technology.

Subsequently, people recognize that the old ways of doing things are changing and are no longer celebrated. This can cause a sense of sadness, loss, and even depression. In addition, people may feel overwhelmed by the new skills and knowledge required to adapt.

Eventually, more individuals and organizations begin to experiment with the new technology as part of the testing phase. Individuals start learning new skills or finding ways to integrate technology into their job or organization.

Finally, everyone comes to acknowledge the benefits and accept the new technology as a part of their lives and day-to-day work.

For organizations, understanding these seven stages is vital for setting realistic expectations, managing internal resistance, and navigating the changes required in order to stay competitive. For individuals, being cognizant of the natural reactions to new technology can spur you into action and help you reach the acceptance stage faster than those around you.

It's worth noting that not every individual or organization will go through all seven stages or experience each stage in the prescribed order. Early adopters, for example, are inclined to embrace new technology overnight, while others may linger in one stage for an extended period and never reach the next stage. The latter can be dangerous as there is an opportunity cost to inaction as others capitalize on the first-mover advantage, which brings us to the missing middle theory.

The Missing Middle

For those looking to thrive in the new era of work, it is critical to understand that AI, in most cases, is designed to enhance productivity rather than to outright replace you. In line with this perspective, many of the jobs of the future are predicted to be copilot roles, in which humans work alongside AI to carry out a variety of professional tasks, whether that's linguists using ChatGPT to translate documents or lawyers validating contracts drafted by AI assistants.

In the healthcare sector, for example, AI can be used to streamline administrative tasks, manage patient records, and even assist in interpreting medical images, allowing medical professionals to spend more quality time with patients and make more informed decisions.

In marketing, AI tools can provide real-time analytics, predictive models, and relevant ad copy, helping marketers make informed decisions and increase the success of their ad campaigns.

By leveraging AI's ability to handle complex calculations and process vast amounts of data, humans across industries can focus more on tasks requiring creativity, emotional intelligence, and critical thinking—skills that are uniquely human. This is the viewpoint championed in the book *Human + Machine: Reimagining Work in the Age of AI*. Termed the *missing middle*, the authors advocate that the most effective and cost-efficient path forward is to merge automated tools with the flexibility of human workers to achieve optimum outcomes.

The principles of cybernetics, as espoused by Norbert Wiener, reinforce the concept of the missing middle and highlight the complementary nature of our respective strengths. Derived from the Greek word *kybernetes*, cybernetics means *steersman* or *governor*, which emphasizes the notions of control, communication, and feedback in systems. While broad in scope, at its core, cybernetics looks at systems and processes that aim to analyze and understand the principles of how to be effective, adaptive, and self-governing. In the context of artificial intelligence, cybernetics looks at how machines can complement and mimic human-like behavior or decision-making processes as part of a symbiotic feedback loop with human operators, as popularized in Norbert Wiener's research.

Born in 1894, Wiener became interested in cybernetics following his involvement in the development of computers and automated anti-aircraft guns during World War II. This included his realization that the process of tracking a moving aircraft entailed making several observations to anticipate its future trajectory. Amid the dynamics of war, he observed that the reactions of the gunner must be factored into predictions. This is due to the fact that pilots alter course in response to enemy fire, prompting the gunner to adjust, thereby creating a feedback loop where the gunner's actions eventually shape their future actions.

Recognizing that feedback loops are all around us, Wiener went on to explore the traits of this phenomenon to optimize human-machine feedback loops under the lens of cybernetics. Wiener posited that when harnessed correctly, technology actually amplifies human capabilities and productivity by extending our cognitive and physical capacities, enabling us to accomplish tasks more efficiently and effectively.

We see this today with AI-powered tools such as Consensus, Elicit, and Semantic Scholar, which allow researchers to find papers, extract key claims or summaries, and even brainstorm their ideas by connecting with a massive pool of academic research. These tools allow researchers to streamline the research process and concentrate on higher-level cognitive activities such as critical thinking, hypothesis formulation, experimental design, and interpretation of results, which can help drive advancements in innovation and scientific understanding.

Although the idea of substituting human tasks with AI tools is alluring, not all tasks should function independently

144

of humans. Instead, most tasks should operate in a feedback loop with human copilots, with AI constantly learning from human inputs and modifying their behavior accordingly. These interconnected feedback systems optimize the strengths of both parties, resulting in new breakthroughs and an overall productivity boost.

Chess, in particular, provides a glimpse into effective collaboration between humans and AI, particularly given chess's longstanding relationship with AI technology. In hybrid chess competitions, human players utilize their creativity and deep understanding of the game to work in tandem with AI chess engines to leverage their vast analytical capabilities. The combination of human ingenuity and AI's analytical prowess creates a synergy that outperforms either side performing on its own. This successful partnership has been demonstrated in a number of tournaments, including freestyle chess competitions, where teams composed of human players and AI engines have consistently outperformed human-only and AI-only teams.

This includes the 2005 Freestyle Chess Tournament held by the Internet Chess Club (ICC), which permitted players to use any combination of computer chess engine, database, and human analysis. The winners weren't grandmasters or supercomputers but two amateur players working together with multiple AI chess machines, defeating both highly ranked human players and standalone chess engines.

Job Replacement & Business Disruption

The speed at which AI is seeping into all aspects of modern work—from marketing to human resources—underscores AI literacy as a key skill set for the modern workforce. Also, just as the Internet Age triggered an avalanche of new job titles, so too will the AI-centric era we are now entering.

During the formative years of the Dot-com evolution, many traditional job opportunities—including travel agent, journalist, courier, stockbroker, and Encyclopaedia

145

salesperson—contracted or were phased out entirely. However, these losses were gradually filled with the creation of new job roles. An explosion of highly skilled jobs ensued in web development, search engine optimization, e-commerce, online customer service, web design, affiliate marketing, and eventually social media and mobile web design. While it's probable that a proportion of these jobs will now be phased out by AI, new job roles will again be created or converted to copilot roles.

Moreover, it's possible that AI may assist in creating more inclusive workplaces. Assistive AI technologies such as AI-driven speech recognition software can help individuals with mobility impairments, while AI-powered predictive text and voice synthesis can assist those with speech difficulties.

Likewise, AI technology will empower smaller companies or companies-of-one to thrive in a more fragmented and fast-paced world. The ability to generate a website, write blog content, and create an explainer video using generative AI tools will allow individuals to test their ideas, gain market feedback, and iterate faster than ever before.

Conversely, labor-intensive organizations that rely on human capital to carry out services such as ghostwriting, translation, and online tutoring are earmarked to be the first affected by AI technology. With AI offering a faster and lower-cost alternative, these organizations may experience a significant transformation in how they operate as well as a negative impact in the short term. Exposing this reality, stocks in the online tutoring company, Chegg, plummeted after the CEO admitted the threat posed by AI. During the company's earnings call in mid-2023, their CEO Dan Rosensweig explained that "In the first part of the year, we saw no noticeable impact from ChatGPT on our new account growth and we were meeting expectations on new sign-ups. However, since March we saw a significant spike in student interest in ChatGPT. We now believe it's having an impact on our new customer growth rate".[15]

---

[15] Prarthana Prakash, "Chegg's shares tumbled nearly 50% after the edtech company said its customers are using chatgpt instead of paying for its study

While it's important to acknowledge that Chegg exceeded profit expectations as a result of the explosive demand for online education during the COVID lockdowns that took place between 2020 and 2021, AI must be considered as a competitive force in all industries, alongside traditional business threats such as globalization and geopolitics.

In response to technological changes introduced by ChatGPT, Chegg has announced that it's developing its own AI, CheggMate, in partnership with OpenAI to assist students with their homework. Textbroker, a content writing service provider, has also added AI technology to its service offering, and many other service platforms will be forced to adapt or die as well.

Human services will remain in demand but rather than being the staple service, they will become a premium or concierge service added on top of a fast and more cost-effective AI-powered service. Tax, legal, and accounting services, for example, will be serviced by AI agents trained on relevant data, and then verified, witnessed, and supplemented by human experts. This creates a new business model where customers can access self-service offerings powered by AI, such as contract drafting or balance sheet generation, and then have the option to communicate or receive personalized assistance from a human assistant as part of a human service that is more focused, personalized, and effective than many of today's basic service offerings.

AI Adoption in Organizations

The adoption of AI presents a range of opportunities for organizations seeking to gain a competitive edge. However, the road to successful AI implementation is not without obstacles. From data quality and availability, to cultural resistance and ethical concerns, various factors can hinder the smooth integration of AI solutions. Implementing AI practices entails significant upfront costs as well, including

tools", *Fortune*, May 3, 2023.

investments in hardware, software, and hiring skilled professionals.

In many cases, organizations may be reluctant to commit substantial resources without a clear understanding of the return on investment and the potential long-term benefits AI can bring. AI processes can also disrupt traditional job roles and workflows, creating anxiety among employees about potential job losses or changes to their responsibilities.

Overcoming these obstacles requires a well-thought-out strategy, including robust data management practices, hiring, training and upskilling employees, thorough cost-benefit analyses, stakeholder involvement, and prioritizing ethical considerations. For small organizations, collaborating with experienced AI vendors and consultants can help to facilitate successful AI integration. However, for medium and large-sized organizations, it's important to follow a top-down approach that can align all the necessary resources and implement organization-wide changes. Under this context, appointing a dedicated Chief AI Officer can play a pivotal role. By appointing a single Chief AI Officer instead of relying on a committee of AI consultants, companies can ensure streamlined implementation and accelerated testing, leading to faster adoption of AI strategies throughout the organization.

Reporting directly to the CEO, CTO, or a board of directors, a Chief AI Officer works as a senior executive responsible for identifying opportunities for AI adoption, ensuring that AI efforts align with the company's overall business objectives. It's important to acknowledge that the Chief AI Officer does not personally code algorithms or lead the data science team's day-to-day operations. Rather, they are responsible for monitoring market changes, determining the right strategic direction, and identifying opportunities for the company to utilize AI technologies effectively in marketing, research and development, and other parts of the organization. By staying ahead of the curve, they guide the organization to ride the AI wave instead of being overwhelmed by it.

In addition, the Chief AI Officer is responsible for engaging with various teams within the organization in order to gather feedback and determine optimal areas for AI application. In the short term, this may involve conducting A/B or split testing to compare human and AI-powered resources, evaluating different AI software, and using testing and data to find quick wins and gain internal support for new practices. By presenting quantifiable metrics and data that highlight the improvements achieved through AI practices, it becomes easier to demonstrate the value that AI brings to the organization.

The Hustle Daily Newsletter, for example, ran an A/B test using custom AI-generated images and human-edited stock photography.[16] The AI-generated version was spun up using Midjourney and designed based on the goal of aligning the image with the ad copy and the value proposition they wanted to communicate. This resulted in a 3x increase in ad performance (measured on the cost to acquire clicks) compared to the classic stock photography approach. On top of this, the AI-generated ads were faster to produce.

THE WORLD IF EVERYONE READ THE HUSTLE DAILY NEWSLETTER

Subscribe for free

---

[16] Marketing Against The Grain, "How A $25B Company Uses A.I. To 300x Their Marketing Results," *HubSpot Podcast Network,* June 13, 2023.

Figure 7: The Hustle Daily ad image created using Midjourney

Hosting a hackathon, spanning an afternoon or a couple of days, is another option to catalyze momentum and explore AI-first processes. Hosting a hackathon not only serves as a litmus test for trialing AI's applicability and effectiveness within the organization but also helps to generate interest and motivation across teams. A hackathon can revolve around a specific theme or problem, where teams collaborate to plan and develop solutions, ultimately presenting their prototypes to key decision-makers or team leaders at the end of the event.

While it's valuable to run internal experiments and consider the benefits that AI can bring, it's important to acknowledge that not all teams, departments, and organizations will need to adopt AI technology. The search engine company DuckDuckGo, for example, has resisted industry trends such as personalized search results, personalized ad targeting, and user data tracking to provide a privacy-centric alternative for users concerned about data privacy and tracking. This includes offering Duck Player mode, which provides users with a clean viewing experience stripped of personalized ads and prevents users' viewing activity from influencing their YouTube recommendations.

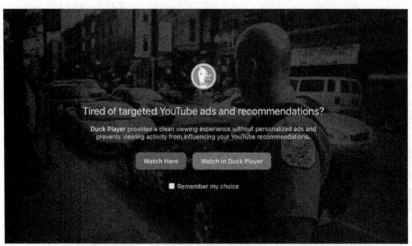

Figure 8: Duck Player mode offers a clean viewing experience without personalized ads

Similarly, Basecamp has chosen not to adopt certain AI-driven features commonly found in other project management tools, instead prioritizing a more human-centric approach to collaboration in its task management software. In a different vein, Luddite Games focuses on developing games that rely on human creativity and decision-making under the game's narrative of destroying AI and saving human jobs.

This type of counterapproach strategy allows each of these companies to differentiate themselves in the market and cater to an audience that values privacy or human involvement and expertise. While it may not be the fastest or most effective path to obtain media interest and investor funding in the early stages of an AI hype cycle, there will be plenty of opportunities for other service providers to target a niche audience by openly resisting AI technology and embracing human expertise. The key is to openly resist new AI technology and integrate this stance into the company's marketing strategy and value proposition rather than being a side-effect of inaction and business model complacency.

Digital Craft & Offline Events

Despite the immense efficiency gains that AI offers, consumers will continue to respect the craft and attention to detail that humans bring to their work. Whether it's creating a piece of artwork or crafting handmade products, we disproportionally value things created by ourselves or other humans. In psychology, this phenomenon is called the "labor illusion", which captures how people perceive a product or service as more valuable or of higher quality when they believe that a considerable amount of human effort and labor was invested in its creation. We see this with birthday and thank you cards. Despite the shareability and convenience of e-cards, most people prefer the thoughtfulness and effort that come with sending a physical card and writing a handwritten message. Similarly, if you browse the comments section on YouTube, you will see users consistently praise video creators who take the time to produce subtitles for their videos, add timestamps, or who spend inordinate amounts of time and effort capturing the perfect drone shot. Ultimately, the human touch carries a sense of quality, uniqueness, and care that resonates with people. In addition, there is an inherent appreciation for the time, skill, and dedication that goes into creating something manually—even if it is done digitally.

In the future, the ubiquity of AI-generated content may lead to a future where creating your own podcast or video content without AI assistance is valued as a form of digital craft. Likewise, companies that offer human customer service support might stand out in a world where AI avatars are trained on millions of data points and customer support logs.

Finally, the surge in AI-generated content may lead to renewed interest in offline events such as meetups, political debates, and music concerts, as a direct response to the growing distrust of online content. In an age of deep fakes and content manipulation, seeking face-to-face interactions may be the only way to discern authenticity and verify what is genuinely real in the world. Likewise, dating might veer towards a return to more in-person encounters or an embrace of Japanese-style single's parties known as goukon[17], countering the influence of AI-enhanced photos and AI-generated conversations in the online dating space. Alternatively, some individuals may find the efficiency of their AI dating agent communicating with a suitor's AI agent and scheduling a coffee date more appealing!

Key Takeaways

1) The fear of job displacement isn't new and while AI is expected to create new roles and demand new skills, we could see a drastic shakeup to knowledge work. This

---

[17] Goukon parties are popular in Japan as a way for adults to socialize and expand their social circles while potentially finding romantic interests. These parties can take various forms, such as dinners, barbecues, or outings to various entertainment venues. The atmosphere is typically more relaxed and informal compared to traditional matchmaking events.

includes humans working together with AI agents as copilots to enhance productivity and efficiency.

2) Resistance is common in the face of technological innovation, with individuals and organizations often going through a series of emotional responses akin to the seven stages of grief.

3) AI technology has the potential to empower smaller companies and individuals to test new ideas at a lower cost.

4) AI-powered service providers can offer faster and low-cost services, challenging traditional business models.

5) Appointing a Chief AI Officer can help organizations navigate AI strategies, identify opportunities, and align AI efforts with overall business objectives.

6) The proliferation and ubiquity of AI technology could pave the way for a new form of digital trade or commerce carried out by humans, without AI involvement.

Thought Exercises

1) What are your strengths and weaknesses? How can AI be used to overcome your weaknesses and spend more time on your strengths?

2) How can AI companies move beyond crude comparisons with humans to measure and market their products? (i.e., new jobs created by AI, lives saved by an AI product).

3) In which industries or scenarios will using AI be a potential disadvantage for the brand, sport, organization, or other entity?

Further Resources

The field of artificial intelligence is vast and multifaceted, encompassing various domains covered in this book. As a result, acquiring knowledge in AI requires deep-diving into an array of different subjects, each one contributing to a more comprehensive understanding. This final chapter provides a general guide to learning resources and an overview of potential career paths.

Formal Education

The most obvious starting point for anyone interested in AI is formal education. Universities around the world offer courses dedicated to AI and related fields, including data science, machine learning, and computer science. Highly respected Master's programs in machine learning are offered at Stanford, Berkeley, Carnegie Mellon, Columbia, University of Washington, and MIT. Other reputable institutes include Edinburgh, Duke, Michigan, University of Pennsylvania, Toronto, UCSD, Brown, UCL, Georgia Tech, Cambridge, Oxford, and Cornell. Carnegie Mellon University, renowned for its Robotics Institute, also provides excellent degree courses in AI robotics. Note too that many colleges offer online degrees and there are various other degree options offered around the world.

Another valuable but more affordable option is the Georgia Tech Online Master of Science in Computer Science (OMSCS) program. Launched in 2014 in collaboration with Udacity and AT&T, this degree is fully online and the curriculum is no different from what you would receive as an on-campus student. The program costs just under USD $10,000 for a one-year full-time degree or a two-year part-time degree.

The program includes specialization tracks in areas such as machine learning and robotics. The machine learning track provides a deep understanding of the key principles and algorithms. The robotics track, meanwhile, teaches you how to design, implement, and analyze modern robotic systems. This track will teach you knowledge regarding the physical embodiment of AI systems, which is a crucial part of how AI interfaces with the real world. However, be wary that the program's rigor and pace are equivalent to its on-campus counterpart, so you will need to be ready to dedicate a significant amount of effort and time to your studies.

After completing a Master's degree in machine learning/artificial intelligence/data science, there is then the option of completing a PhD. This is an ideal route for those wishing to delve deeper into AI topics.

PhDs in many countries are supported by government or university funding. There is, though, a sizeable opportunity cost of completing a four-year PhD on a basic salary/stipend over working in industry on a full-time salary. In places like the United States, you can expect to receive USD $20,000-45,000 a year to complete a PhD course, compared to earning an annual salary of USD $80,000-120,000 working for a private company.

However, Google, Facebook, and Microsoft have been known for raiding the ranks of academia to recruit talent in the space of artificial intelligence and to secure a pipeline of young talent. The prevailing logic is that hiring professors unlocks a new network of talent and makes it easier to hire former PhD students. The other upside of completing a PhD is that you have greater control over the scope of your work and research, and the academic path overall may be a more attractive proposition for some people.

Non-Degree Options

Beyond traditional education pathways, there is a plethora of non-degree options delivered online. Online learning platforms have democratized access to knowledge, offering a range of courses catering to various specializations. This includes platforms like Coursera and edX which partner with top universities and industry leaders to provide high-quality, accessible content. For example, Coursera's *AI For Everyone* course, developed by

Andrew Ng, a co-founder of Coursera and an adjunct professor at Stanford University, offers a non-technical introduction to AI.

As my preferred non-degree option, I recommend DataCamp as an excellent resource for learning about AI, machine learning, data science, and related fields including how to code. The platform's approach is hands-on, focusing on active learning and practical application, which is quite different from traditional lecture-based courses. Each skill-based course is broken down into bite-sized lessons combining short videos with immediate hands-on exercises.

Books

There is a wealth of books that delve into AI from different perspectives. For those interested in the philosophical and societal impacts of AI, books such as Nick Bostrom's *Superintelligence: Paths, Dangers, Strategies* and Max Tegmark's *Life 3.0: Being Human in the Age of Artificial Intelligence* are highly recommended. If you're interested in the technical aspects, O'Reilly Media textbooks such as *Hands-On Machine Learning with Scikit-Learn, Keras, and TensorFlow* authored by Aurélien Géron provide practical insights for developers into AI, deep learning, and machine learning.

Real-World Projects

For hands-on learning, nothing beats working on real-world projects. As a platform for data science competitions and public datasets, Kaggle offers a plethora of datasets and challenges that can be used to hone your skills in machine learning and AI.

Contributing to open-source AI projects is another way to gain practical experience. Projects such as OpenAI's GPT models, TensorFlow, and PyTorch all welcome community contributions.

In regard to practical training, LeWagon offers data science boot camps around the world, which train students with the practical skills needed to become a data scientist and work in a data team. LeWagon offers a lot of free online and offline events, which you can sign up for on their website (www.lewagon.com).

Blogs & Podcasts

Podcasts and blogs are valuable resources for learning about AI. Podcasts such as *The AI Alignment Podcast* by the Future of Life Institute, *Data Skeptic*, and *AI in Business* all provide insightful discussions on various AI topics. Blogs such as *Towards Data Science* and the *Google AI Blog* also offer deep dives into AI trends and research. My favorite podcast is the OC Devel *Machine Learning Guide* podcast.

Potential Career Paths in AI

Whether you're a recent graduate or a seasoned professional considering a career switch, there is a place and role for you in the ever-broadening world of AI. As Stuart Russell and Peter Norvig point out in *Artificial Intelligence: A Modern Approach*, AI is a broad and rapidly evolving field that offers a plethora of opportunities for those willing to invest the time and effort required to master it.

As the influence and impact of AI grows, the demand for professionals in this field will also continue to rise. Regardless of industry or geography, organizations across the globe are recognizing the power of AI to drive growth, innovation, and efficiency. This section focuses on the vast array of career paths in AI and provides a broad view of the roles, skills, and opportunities available for those interested in this field.

AI Research Scientist

The first role we'll examine is the AI research scientist. This position is typically based in academia or research institutions but some private sector companies employ research scientists too. These professionals are the thought

157

leaders of AI, pushing the boundaries of what's possible. In addition to publishing papers and attending conferences, they are often found working on abstract and complex problems in machine learning, deep learning, and other AI-related fields. They possess a deep understanding of algorithms, calculus, linear algebra, and statistics. While a doctoral degree in a related field is often required, some organizations hire candidates with a Masters degree and substantial relevant experience.

AI Engineers

AI engineers apply the theories and concepts developed by AI research scientists in real-world scenarios. They build, test, and deploy AI models and manage AI systems and infrastructure. They must be proficient in various programming languages like Python, Java, or C++, and be familiar with AI libraries such as TensorFlow or PyTorch. A Bachelors or Masters degree in computer science, data science, or a related field is usually required, along with a strong practical understanding of machine learning.

Data Scientists

Data scientists work as the detectives of the AI world. They sift through large volumes of data, using machine learning and statistical models to extract meaningful insights that can be used to solve business problems and make strategic decisions. They require a firm grasp of statistics, as well as experience with programming languages and data management tools.

Machine Learning Engineers

Straddling the roles of AI engineer and data scientist, machine learning engineers are typically tasked with creating data models that are then implemented by AI applications to learn and improve. To work as a machine learning engineer, you will need to have a deep understanding of multiple programming languages, machine learning algorithms, and data modeling.

AI Ethicists

AI ethicists represent a newer but increasingly important role in the field of AI. As AI applications proliferate, questions about their ethical implications and the governance required to ensure their fair use have expanded too. AI ethicists analyze and address these issues. Their backgrounds can vary widely, from philosophy to law to data science, with the common denominator being a dual understanding of AI technologies and a strong ethical framework.

AI Policy Advocates

A lesser-known but growing role is the AI policy advocate. These professionals work with governments, non-profit organizations, and companies to influence policy and legislation related to AI. This role requires a strong understanding of AI, public policy, and legal frameworks.

The roles mentioned represent just a snapshot of the opportunities available in the field of AI. Each of these roles offers a unique perspective on AI and serves a critical function in its ongoing development. However, all these roles share a common need for continuous learning and adaptation. Given the rapid pace of advancements in AI, professionals in this field must be committed to staying up-to-date with the latest developments.

Before deciding on a career path in AI, it's important to consider your interests, strengths, and long-term career goals too. For example, if you're passionate about researching new theories and technologies, a career as an AI research scientist might be a good fit for you. If you are more interested in applying AI technologies to solving real-world problems, roles such as AI engineer or data scientist might be a better match.

Moreover, each of these roles offers different levels of interaction with others. Some roles, such as AI engineer or machine learning engineer, may work as part of a larger team and interact closely with other departments. Other roles such as AI research scientist may have a more solitary focus and work primarily on individual projects.

Finally, it's crucial to consider the societal implications of AI in choosing a potential career path. As AI becomes more integrated into our daily lives, there is a growing need for professionals who can address the ethical, legal, and societal implications of AI. Roles such as AI ethicist or AI policy advocate are expected to become increasingly important as the field continues to evolve.

Other Books By The Author

Generative AI Art for Beginners
Master the use of text prompts to generate stunning AI art in seconds.

ChatGPT Prompts Book
Maximize your results with ChatGPT using a series of proven text prompt strategies.

Machine Learning for Absolute Beginners
Learn the fundamentals of machine learning, explained in plain English.

Machine Learning with Python for Beginners
Progress your career in machine learning by learning how to code in Python and build your own prediction models to solve real-life problems.

Machine Learning: Make Your Own Recommender System
Learn how to make your own machine learning recommender system in an afternoon using Python.

Data Analytics for Absolute Beginners
Make better decisions using every variable with this deconstructed introduction to data analytics.

Statistics for Absolute Beginners
Master the fundamentals of inferential and descriptive statistics with a mix of practical demonstrations, visual examples, historical origins, and plain English explanations.

Python for Absolute Beginners
Master the essentials of Python from scratch with beginner-friendly guidance.

Printed in Great Britain
by Amazon

41899391R00096